Joyful Cooking

IN THE PURSUIT OF GOOD HEALTH

The following recipes have been reprinted with permission from the Weston Price Foundation: Raw Milk Formula, Goat Milk Formula, and Liver Formula

The material is for educational purposes only and is not intended as diagnosis, treatment or prescription for any disease. Nutritional balancing and hair tissue mineral analysis is a method of assessing and correcting imbalances and is not a replacement for regular medical care. Neither the publisher nor author shall be liable or responsible for any loss or damage allegedly arising from any information or suggestion in this book.

To order books, please visit: www.joyfeldman.com

ATTENTION UNIVERSITIES, COLLEGES AND PROFESSIONAL ORGANIZATIONS: Quantity discounts are available on bulk purchases of this book for educational, or gift purposes. Please contact Joy@joyfeldman.com

ISBN: 978-0-615-43307-3

Joy Feldman
JHF Nutritional Counsulting
Wickford Chiropractic and Wellness Center
610 Ten Rod Road Unit 1
North Kingstown, Rhode Island 02852

www.joyfeldman.com

Printed in the United States of America

Design & Illustrations by Beth Slocum - Woodhaus Studio

The Text of this book was composed in Archer & Avenir

Joyful Cooking

IN THE PURSUIT OF GOOD HEALTH

RESTORE & HEAL THROUGH NUTRITIONAL BALANCING

OVER 100 RECIPES FOR BOTH YOUNG AND OLD

By Joy Feldman

Foreword By Lawrence Wilson, M.D.

Newly Revised and Updated

www.joyfeldman.com

NOTES ON THE REVISED EDITION:

The principal traditions and teachings of this volume were not revised, but rather they were expanded on in response to new, updated information. Additionally, there are new chapters and additional information on foods, natural baby formulas, weight loss supplements, and general health. Many new recipes have been added as well with some new food for thought.

May your health grow and flower, nourishing you each day.

Praise for *Joyful Cooking in the Pursuit of Good Health*

❝ Joyful cooking in the pursuit of good health, is a wonderful educational experience for all who use it. I cannot recommend it highly enough. Not only does it teach principles of nutrition, but provides many tasty, simple recipes that will make eating healthfully a pleasure as well. ❞

Lawrence Wilson, M.D. Author of *Nutritional Balancing, Sauna Therapy And The Real Self*

❝ Finally, a cookbook that makes health a top priority! Joy takes us through the "why's and how's" of creating delicious, healthy meals in a quick and easy fashion. Beyond all the wonderful recipes, she shares basic fundamentals of healthy cooking with ideas for artisitic exploration with food and spices. Her tips for feeding fussy children are priceless.❞

Megan Lorimer, M.A.C.

❝ 'The Pursuit of Good Health' sounded like a terrific but unattainable ideal until I started following the simple guidelines in 'Joyful Cooking'. The nutritional information is easy to grasp, essential to know and a cinch to implement. Within a month, I've lost that caffeine craving, boosted my energy and dropped those annoying pounds I thought had made a permanent home on my hips. Scrumptious recipes, quick preparation, better health and no yawning at the keyboard. ❞

Lisa Reitman-Dobi, Playwright/Columnist

❝ An excellent guide to helping those who want to understand and improve their health through diet! The recipes are easy to follow and the food tastes delicious. ❞
MDF, M.D.

"At last a groundbreaking and insightful informative book done in a user friendly and all inclusive format, delivering a pinpoint focus on the healing powers and life enrichment of often overshadowed simplified real whole foods nutrition. What this book offers is nothing short of a breath of vital fresh life force to those seeking methods to rid the body of dis-ease and start eating and living as if life really matters. ❞
Ramsay Mead, RYT, CN

*This book
is dedicated
to you...*

*All of you
who are in pursuit
of good health.*

FOREWORD

Nutritional balancing science is an advanced method of healing the body that draws upon Western medical sciences, and other ancient healing wisdom. Nutritional balancing helps restore the body's vitality and energy-producing capacity by gently but powerfully balancing body chemistry, rather than through the use of many remedies.

A critical aspect of nutritional balancing is often a person's diet. The diet requires mainly cooked vegetables, cooked animal protein and a minimum of sugars, sweet foods and processed foods. Learning how to cook and consume more of the right foods is perhaps the most important dietary change needed by millions of people around the globe, and especially in America.

Joy Feldman's book, *Joyful Cooking In The Pursuit of Good Health*, provides many excellent and simple recipes, with many pages of general nutritional information along with practical how-to instructions. Her book differs from all others because it specifically explains the essential dietary principles of nutritional balancing science and how to apply them in the kitchen. These include the metabolic typing concepts developed by Dr. Paul C. Eck, the founder of nutritional balancing, and why cooked food is preferred, even though many current health authorities suggest eating more raw foods. *Ex: An important reason to avoid most raw vegetables is the difficulty absorbing the minerals and other nutrients it contains.* Our bodies simply do not digest cellulose very well. Cooking breaks down some of the fiber, releasing the minerals to our bodies. Cooking also reduces the volume of many vegetables, allowing one to eat more of the precious, mineral-rich vegetables. Joy also explains why one should avoid wheat, most beef, most fruit and all sweets while offering the reader, simple recipes they may fix at home in their pursuit of good health. By offering humanity this book, Joy has rendered a great service. I am truly grateful to her for this.

LAWRENCE WILSON, M.D.

TABLE OF CONTENTS

ACKNOWLEDGEMENTS

*This book was made possible by the support,
love and encouragement of many.*

*I owe Dr. Larry Wilson a debt of gratitude for his guidance and direction
as he assisted me in my journey back to health. As I found out what my body
was lacking and what I needed to omit from my diet, I regained
my well-being in a matter of months. Dr. Wilson, M.D., a wonderful physician
and inspirational mentor, guided me as I created a nutritional
dietary tome that outlines a holistic approach towards good health. Dr. Wilson
gave his time, his feedback and shared his knowledge so that
I could create a volume that would give others an opportunity to find their
way back to health. For all of his help, I am enormously grateful.*

*Many thanks to all my clients who have guided, encouraged me, and
provided me with feedback along the way.*

*Finally, and most importantly, I thank my family without whom
I could not have fought my way back to health, nor created this book that
I hope will help others recover and thrive as well. My mother and son
patiently edited, always asking thought provoking questions that had me
rethinking sections of this book. Thank you two so much for all of your
time and assistance. And thank you to my daughter, who was always
by my side in the kitchen helping me create new recipes. My husband, Michael,
has given me the love and support I needed to stay on the path and to see
this project through to completion. His unwavering strength calmed
me when I was overwhelmed by the many different challenges I faced as
I took this book from conception to publication. I am fortunate that my
family has always inspired me to grow, learn and create. Their
steadfast encouragement has allowed me to pursue
my dreams and watch them blossom into realized goals.*

PREFACE

Are you confused about which foods to eat? If so, you are not alone. Today, perhaps more than ever, it is a daunting task to decide which foods are the healthiest choices. Eating wholesome, well-rounded meals are complicated by the multitude of conflicting opinions given by both medical and nutritional professionals. Popular mythologies range from diets that have copious amounts of fats to those that remove fats completely. The oft-repeated questions "Who is right? What is best?"

However, the most important questions are: "What is best for your health? What is right for you?"

By discovering your body's specific needs and deficiencies, you can reclaim energy and good health. By educating yourself and understanding several basic facts about nutrition and cooking, you can easily enjoy menus that boost vitality, while also leaving confusing jargon as well as time-consuming, complex diets behind.

Understanding the importance of an optimal nutritional program is more relevant than ever. There has never been a time in our country during which Americans have eaten so poorly. We have abandoned nourishing proteins, fats, and vegetables and have replaced them with processed foods, fast-foods and snack-foods that contain no more than scant by-products, additives and preservatives. Countless products promoted as elixirs for better health are actually lower in value than easily procured and prepared produce; glitzy packaging, high budget advertising and multi-media marketing have taken the place of wholesome, quality ingredients.

For instance, take Kellogg's Cocoa Puffs®. Recently, the company emblazoned a banner across the front of their cereal box that stated that their cereal, "Now helps support your child's immunity." Yet, highly processed sugar-laden cereal is not a medicine, nor does it enhance immune function. What is even scarier is that the FDA supported this health claim. This factory-created food did contain some immune boosting vitamins, but it certainly did not contain enough to establish wellness. If you look more closely at the ingredient list, Kellogg's® also added into this concoction of ingredients processed white sugar, partially hydrogenated trans-fats oils, and synthetic chemical vitamins and chemical preservatives.

These combinations of ingredients in actuality are anti-nutrients, substances that interfere with the performance of one or more nutrients needed by the body, ultimately resulting in a product that lowers immunity. The claim advertised on the cereal boxes misleads consumers by having them believe they were eating healthy, beneficial foods when in reality, they were not.

Today so many people are confused as to what foods they should eat. Misinformation and faulty health claims are abundant. Every year 17,000 new products are being placed on food shelves with toxic ingredients promising health, yet they are poorly supported by proper scientific evidence.[1]

Unlike our ancestors, we have an unprecedented array of foods from which to choose. And with this, we also have an unprecedented rise in obesity, osteoporosis, cancer, allergies, asthma, mental illness, birth defects, ulcers and emphysema.[2] Greater options do not necessarily translate to greater value when it comes to diet and nutrition.

Sadly, it seems as though society has forgotten that our natural state is one of balance and vitality. Simple preparation of nutrient-rich foods can be easy, and is what keeps a body healthy. Yet, our ancestors did not have the range of modern appliances and availability of foods, but they had the advantage of using whole foods, unprocessed and unrefined products, rather than filling up on empty calories. Choosing the proper foods will help restore your energy, bringing wellness and healing into your life. The correct foods for your body have the power to heal, just as the wrong foods can trigger illness and rapid aging. *Joyful Cooking in the Pursuit of Good Health* is more than a cookbook. It's an information resource. Understanding which foods are best for you is the key to more energy and better health. Creative recipes use high yield ingredients and optimal, yet simple, preparation techniques. The dietary guidelines outlined in this book require a minimal amount of effort. Simple, nutrient rich ingredients that are easily prepared allow everyone to follow this program. Little spare time does not mean you have to eat unappetizing meals. On the contrary: wholesome foods, simply prepared, allow you to savor superb natural flavors and juices, pleasing the palate and fortifying the body. Delicious meals do not require a great deal of effort, expertise or excessive cost.

My personal experience with nutritional balancing science[3], hair tissue mineral analysis[4] and the diet outlined in this book allowed me to regain my health and energy. This wellness guide and collection of recipes was borne out of the work I did for myself and—subsequently—for my clients. Nutrition and an awareness of what my body lacked—as well as what it needed to eliminate—provided me with a way back to enjoying life. I am extremely happy to share what I have learned. It is my hope that *Joyful Cooking In the Pursuit of Good Health* will help you live life filled with balance, well-being and happiness, and, of course, much joy.

Here's to your health!

Food shall be your medicine and medicine shall be your food.

Hippocrates

IN THE PURSUIT OF GOOD HEALTH

A BOUQUET OF LIGHT

My journey began after the birth of my first child. My illness started subtly. I began to tire easily. I experienced an onset of joint pain as well as stiffness that eventually affected my entire body. The physical discomfort became so intense that walking became laborious and painful. As my joints became stiffer and more "locked up," even sitting hurt. When my newborn son would cry from his crib, I had to crawl on all fours to get to his room and used his crib as a grip to pull myself up. All the delight I felt at being a mother for the first time, was shadowed by excruciating pain. The joints in my fingers were so swollen and red, that I could not pull the Velcro® off of his diapers.

When you have come to the edge of all light that you know and are about to drop off into the darkness of the unknown, faith is knowing one of two things will happen: There will be something solid to stand on or you will be taught to fly.

Patrick Overton

After rounds of testing, I was diagnosed with an auto-immune disease, though precisely what kind I had remained unclear. I began treatment with powerful medications. The side effects were horrible and I felt more debilitated each day. My daily existence was an effort. The simplest of tasks took a "Herculean effort". I found myself in a mapless terrain of illness, a flat, uncontoured land where no change seemed possible. I was scared. Feeling completely alone, fear and darkness ribboned through me. I was unsure of what was next.

After a move across the country to a new state, I was determined not to spend my life exhausted, weak and in pain. I had a new baby, and I wanted to take care of that bundle of joy—my light, and live my life filled with energy and vitality. Knowing that the way out of the pain was through it, I sought the gap—an opening, a gap of light between the shades of darkness. That gap, created the openness, the space I needed to step outside of my fear, and come forward in faith as it is the light that urges the heart to open to the world. With time and patience, this gap of light, turned into a bouquet of light filled with the strength of courage, warmth of love and the unwavering faith I needed to heal. I elected to make wise choices about what I could change, and move forward into the unknown terrain of the next moment. I began to sense a new direction. I set my intention on healing, and in some unknown way, it rippled out.

By a series of synchronistic events, I became connected with Dr. Larry Wilson, M.D., who studied with Dr. Paul Eck, the founder of nutritional balancing. He clipped my hair, recommended a new diet, along with multiple modalities that would complement my healing —nutritional changes, lifestyle modifications and meditation.

> To keep the body in good health is a duty... Otherwise we shall not be able to keep our mind strong and clear.
>
> *Hindu Prince Gautam Siddharta, founder of Buddhism*

Each suggestion influenced the state of my improved health. Nutrition taught me that there is nothing more amazing than the human body. By choosing natural, nutrient-rich foods, I learned that I could restore my energy and that by eating inflammatory foods—sugars and processed foods, I could trigger illness. Lifestyle changes taught me to sleep more so that my body could heal and meditation shifted my life outlook, teaching me to listen to my body. For too many years, I ignored my body's cues, consciously blinding myself from the link between my actions and my body's healthful state. However, I realized through the practice of meditation that I was disconnected and detached from my own needs, thoughts, and emotions. If I continued to live in this manner, unaware and disconnected from myself, I would not find health. For the first time in many years, I stood inside of my own truth. It was both powerful and frightening. I became more self-reflective, and reconnected with myself; I was attuned to my body and to my mind. I began to uncover a much needed sense of balance in my life.

My recovery was quick, something I would have never dreamed possible after the terrible onslaught of pain and exhaustion I had once experienced. Within a few months, I was off my medications, my energy improved and I was on the road to recovery. After several months under Dr. Wilson's care, the lab report on all my blood tests showed normal results. It took me almost a full year to feel like myself, but everyday, I was encouraged by more energy, less pain and constant progress.

Having regained my own health, I am fortunate to help others regain theirs. Because of my personal health triumph, I believe that you too can restore your health. To begin the pursuit of good health, I urge you to educate yourself and make the changes that will get you into the best condition possible. I will lay the road map out for you; I need you to gas up your car for the journey.

WHY IS HEALTH IMPORTANT?

According to Hippocrates, "The wise man should consider that health is the greatest of human blessings." It is the root source of your preservation. Fundamental to your existence, to how you function and think, to how you feel mentally and emotionally, to how you adapt and respond to your environment, health is at the core of your essence. For adults, good health allows you to work each day, to earn a living, to be productive, to be a better person or even a better parent, as well as to achieve your goals in life. Moreover, good health enables you to enjoy life, be vital—resilient and adaptable.

Poor health prevents you from taking pleasure in all that life has to offer. In fact, many individuals today lack excellent health. Their vitality is low or compromised spurring illness and weak energy reserves in their bodies. They face paralyzing exhaustion and crippling fatigue tangled with other debilitating health issues. Just look at the staggering statistics today. Chronic diseases are now the number one cause of disability and death in the United States. Seven in ten deaths each year have been attributed to cancer, heart disease, and diabetes. One hundred and thirty three million Americans live with at least one chronic disease, and more than one in ten have three or more. Statistically speaking, chronic and degenerative diseases are spiraling out of control. It's time to take charge of your health. It's time for a new beginning; it's time for a change.

A LEOPARD CAN CHANGE ITS SPOTS

Do you want vibrant health? Are you ready to regain your vigor? Do you want to have improved energy, clarity of mind, and enthusiasm for life? Of course. We all want to feel great. But it's often a challenge to know where to begin. And change is often an intimidating proposition. It is not difficult to be healthy, creative and industrious. Rather, this challenge simply warrants that you shift your intention and make new choices.

Where there is great love there are always miracles.

Willa Cather

Life is a matter of making choices.

YOUR BASIC TOOLS: UNCOVERING A PLAN

SELF-LOVE: A CHANGE OF HEART

The first step towards the road to recovery begins with self-love, the ability to feel warmth, caring and concern for oneself. By befriending yourself, you uproot any fear, anger or guilt that keeps you from reclaiming your wellness path. According to the Buddha, " you can search throughout the entire universe for someone who is more deserving of your love and affection than you are yourself, and that person is not to be found anywhere." The truth is that there is no one more deserving of your love and affection than you. Consciously choosing to honor and love "who you are", completely and fully, enables the healing process to begin.

TO LOVE YOURSELF IS TO:

- *Accept and love yourself for the fact that you exist, rather than for what you do.*

- *Place no condition on yourself as to how you behave or what to be in order to receive self-love.*

WHEN YOU DO LOVE YOURSELF, YOU FEEL:

- *You have value and worth.*

- *Warm, cared for and nurtured.*

- *You are perfect just the way you are.*

- *There are no conditions set for your relationship with yourself.*

WHEN YOU DO NOT LOVE YOURSELF THEN YOU FEEL:

- *You might act in ways that are not in accordance with your own beliefs and feelings.*

- *Live your life pleasing others, rather than yourself.*

- *Need others to make you feel good about yourself.*

- *Become your own worst critic who is never able to say you are good enough.*

- *Believe that you can never fail because you would not be worthy of love.*

HOW TO UNCONDITIONALLY LOVE YOURSELF:

- *Identify what conditions you place on yourself so that you love yourself. (For example, I need to be thinner, or prettier to love who I am.)*

- *Analyze why these expectations or conditions you have set for yourself and why they stop you from loving yourself unconditionally. Are these conditions reasonable, rational or even realistic? Develop another way to look at the situation in order to free yourself from this constraint.*

- *Do your best to eliminate these conditions and work on accepting yourself freely, generously and with no limitations.*

- *Loving yourself is the unconditional acceptance of who you are, and asks you to be fully responsible for your own actions. Forgive yourself and others.*

WHAT IS LOVING-KINDNESS MEDITATION?

A beautiful way to make the transition to greater friendliness to oneself is through loving-kindness meditation. Sharon Salzberg, author of *Loving-Kindness*, has done an outstanding job of bringing this important meditation work forward. With these contemplations you can develop self-love by cultivating kindness and compassion, qualities that live within you. By embracing this practice, it helps to develop positive feelings towards oneself through a journey of self-discovery. Allowing you to be your own true friend, this simple practice empowers you to rediscover what is possible for you.

An important point of this meditation is not to try to change who you are, instead this practice asks that you simply befriend yourself. This involves being gentle. Gentleness is a sense of loving-kindness towards oneself. This practice helps to break habits of meanness and self- judgment, freeing your mind to rest from your own inner dialogue. It can help you feel at ease, and at peace. You will soon learn that inside of you, already dwells a place of peace and great strength.

I invite you to practice loving-kindness towards yourself. It does not take long to learn this practice. Remember to do it as often as you can, and help yourself to be successful by bringing your full attention to your meditation.

To begin this meditation, sit comfortably and close your eyes. Silently repeat the following phrases, gathering your intention behind each statement. Try repeating these words each day and watch your heart open and your self-love blossom.

THE MEDITATION IS AS FOLLOWS:

May I be safe.
(Live in safety, free from harm)

May I be at peace.
(Mental happiness)

May I be healthy.
(Freedom from pain, and illness)

May I live with ease.
(Family life, element of daily life, things go easy)

Now, my hope is that you have loving, warm feelings inside. May the wisdom of loving-kindness become a part of your life each and everyday.

PERSONAL RESPONSIBILITY

The next step requires that you take personal responsibility for yourself. As the owner of your health, you are now accountable for what is within your own power, control, or management. It is up to you to choose the direction for your health and recognize that you are the only one who is in charge of your choices. Once you resolve to no longer be a passive observer of your health, content to just let things happen to you or accept whatever might come your way, you will have the power to select better options. Recognizing and reclaiming your power is central to the path of healing.

With this newly found power, you will release old habits and attempt new approaches. This can be challenging, but in change there is power. Once you feel empowered, you are one step closer to improving your health. By discarding old habits, you'll have room for more healthful alternatives, and by letting go of old patterns of behavior, you will create space for new, more effective and healthful ways of living. When you alter your lifestyle and modify your food choices, you'll give yourself a gift: the opportunity to be a healthy, productive and a happy individual.

SPRINGING INTO ACTION

Many of us have little sense of our true strength. We are stronger than we know. I am asking you to uncover your sense of perseverance and commit yourself to the path of healing. To accomplish this, the concepts below will enable you to focus on reclaiming your personal resiliency. By introducing the following steps into your life, you can begin to put these new suggestions into action:

JUST DO IT—ALL YOU NEED TO DO IS JUST SHOW UP

DESIRE to wish for, long for, crave and want. It is the motivating force for whatever we set our minds to obtain. Impelling one to the attainment of something, this strong desire for health is absolutely necessary for healing to take place as everything can be changed easily by connecting with what you want.

INTENTION an act or instance of determining mentally some action or result. It is about maintaining your desires in a consistent way, no matter what happens in the big picture. Try thinking of this idea as persistence, a tenacity to maintain your intention that will lead to consistent results.

ALLOWING to give permission for the process of healing to occur. Helpful pointers to ensure success include:

SLOWING DOWN
Do not schedule your entire day and evening. The more time you have available in your life, the more space you create to process events, feelings and illnesses.

RESTING MORE
The more you rest, the more you accelerate the healing process. If possible, sleep more than 10 hours a night and take naps during the day.

RELAXING
If you are relaxed, the healing process will move along much faster and usually much more easily. Fighting it does no good, except to extend it and make it more severe.

ENLISTING ENCOURAGING SUPPORT
Please know your support people well and do not hesitate to contact them if you need encouragement. Do not enlist people who will minimize your experience or criticize the path you have chosen.

SURRENDER to relinquish or yield to the power of another. Even though you state that you are not sure what the outcome will be, you have faith. It is admitting that you do not know all the facts, rather, it is a surrender to the higher self. This process, requires digging deeply into oneself and trusting in the process.

Give these suggestions a try. Make your health a priority. Love yourself. Be in charge of your body. Chart a new path towards health. Keep hope and joy in your heart. Delight in the pleasure of seeing yourself heal.

CHAPTER
one

we are what we eat

Have we forgotten that excellent food is the basis for our health? What has happened to our nutritional intelligence? Sometime during the last few decades, Americans have lost their dietary sense. Nutritional guidelines that have been passed down from generation to generation have been shunned.

According to Eric Schlosser, author of *Fast Food Nation*, nearly ninety percent of the money Americans spend on food is used to buy processed food—"food that either has no taste or has its tastes constructed from non-nutritive and even harmful additives." Sadly, we have discounted the concept that the most powerful medical tool at our disposal is the fork.

The truth is that when you eat better, you feel better. But for many of us, what to eat can be confusing and at times complicated. It is time to get back to the basics, eating simply. Proteins, vegetables, and healthy fats build the body and improve health. Preservatives, additives, chemicals, toxic metals, hybridized and genetically modified foods, refined sugars and other common invented food like items, diminish vitality.

Tell me what you eat, and I shall tell you what you are.

Jean-Anthelme Brillat-Savarin (1755-1826)

WHAT'S HAPPENED TO OUR FOOD?

Shopping was easy when foods came from a farm. Now, foods are made in a factory, laden with chemical additives. Suddenly, grocery stores are filled with pre-packaged boxes of manufactured foods that tout quick meals in a box. Most of us are unable to pronounce the names of these ingredients. Acesulfame-K, Propylene Glycol Alginate, Butulated Hydroxyanisole, and Butylated Hydroxytoluene are just a few ingredients added to foods as chemical additives. Reading an ingredient list on packaged foods today, reads similar to an organic chemistry textbook. These multi-syllabic formulations are linked to various health conditions, including but not limited to, neurological, intestinal and respiratory conditions. Due to processing methods, certain growing practices, and many other toxic substances, our bodies are being assaulted by these contaminants.

TOXIC METALS & OUR FOOD SUPPLY

Our food supply today is exposed to many environmental contaminants. According to Dr. Larry Wilson, M.D., "when the body does not receive enough essential mineral rich elements, it will pick up whatever toxic metals are available as a substitute." These minerals are important for the body because they are needed to help produce energy. In order to protect the body against these toxic metals, it is important to eat an abundance of mineral rich food. It will actually safeguard the body against the utilization of the toxic metals.

SO WHAT CAUSES THE CONTAMINATION OF BOTH ORGANIC AND NON-ORGANIC FOODS?

- *Tainted irrigation water.*

- *Sewage sludge, fish meal and seaweed are contaminated products commonly used as fertilizers.*

- *Food grown near highways or near industrial plants may contain too much lead and other toxins.*

- *Food preservation, processing, refining, transportation and packaging add contaminants to some degree. For example, copper, aluminum and other toxic substances can be found in the water used to produce breads, cakes, or other prepared foods.*

(See Appendix C for more information on Toxic Metals.)

If organic farming is the natural way, shouldn't organic produce just be called "produce" and make the pesticide—laden stuff take the burden of an adjective.

Ymber Delec

FOOD AFFECTS OUR HEALTH

There is nothing more amazing than the human body; a hundred trillion-cell assemblage that not only boasts the most impressive design, but also exhibits unsurpassed resiliency and healing capacities. However, to keep this finely tuned machine in tip top shape, we need to honor and respect it, and most importantly, we need to recognize that we derive our energy from the foods we consume.

Just think, for a car to run properly it needs the correct fuel or it will not run well. Can you imagine if you put milk in your car's engine? It would not go. Same with the body, it too needs the proper type of fuel to optimize energy production. Choosing to drink soda pop will not result in ideal energy production. It is an improper fuel, lacking in nutrients.

What our bodies need are real whole foods. These nutrient rich provisions provide not only excellent fuel for our bodies, but also preserves the integrity of each cell of the body. What we choose to put in our mouths—will constitute our bodies—our cells—and fuel us with energy. We literally are what we eat and digest.

Did you ever consider what happens when you consume food? What about junk food? Sadly, we believe that our bodies simply can handle anything we put in them. Many do not stop and think that the candy bar they consume or the diet soda they drink will comprise their cellular structure, becoming a part of their heart cells, muscle cells or skin cells.

Make food simple and let things taste of what they are.

Curnonsky (Maurice Edmond Sailand)
French writer (1872-1956)

Consuming artificially manufactured food like products—food imposters—can damage the delicate balance in the body. These artificial triggers damage cells, disrupt hormonal balance, change metabolism, and cause inappropriate growth.[5] Moreover, these artificially created novelties, specifically their artificial colors, flavors, sweeteners and chemical additives, bamboozle the senses we rely on to assess these foods and handle them, according to Joan Gussow, professor of Nutrition at Columbia University and author of *The Organic Life*. Contrastingly, eating natural whole foods has the opposite effect on the body. Welcomed by the senses, these foods build, nourish, sustain, promote and energize physiologic processes that optimize healing and promote health.

Inextricably tied to the construction and maintenance of ideal physiological health is the quality of what you consume. What you eat invariably affects your well-being on the most basic cellular level in the body. When building a house, you must first have top-notch building materials or the house will eventually collapse. This same concept also applies to the human anatomy. Construction of a vibrant body, necessitates a diet filled with first rate building materials, nutrient rich foods or illness will result.

Let's take a carrot for example. When you eat a carrot, a nutrient rich vegetable, it plays a role in the construction of your physiological health. It contains beta-carotene, which helps to protect vision, especially night vision. Beta-carotene converts to Vitamin A in the liver and then begins its journey to the retina, where it changes into rhodopsin, a purple pigment necessary for night vision.

And what about our mental health? Omega-3 fatty acids found in fish are another example of "you are what you eat". Since our brains are composed of fatty acids, the absence of these fats can change our behavior. Research suggests that consuming Omega-3 fatty acids can reduce depression, aggression, anger and improve mental well-being. Quite literally, food for thought.

So what happens when you ingest invented foods? Not only do these foods damage cellular integrity and upset hormonal function in the body, they also lack premium nutrient building compounds. Even if imposter foods are enriched with vitamins, they often contain many health detractors, such as sugar, trans-fats and chemical additives that weaken the body. These invented foods do not equate to what is found in whole foods.

To prove the point that enriched invented foods are not equal to whole food, let's examine the relationship between beta-carotene and cancer. The study first showed a link between consuming whole foods high in beta-carotene, such as carrots, with a decreased risk of cancer. As a result of this observation, an additional study was conducted to see if beta-carotene, itself, prevented cancer. In the experiment, synthetic beta-carotene did not by itself protect against cancer. Instead, the study found that people who smoked had higher rates of cancer when given the synthetic beta-carotene supplement than smokers who did not take the supplement.[6] Synthetic beta-carotene does not provide the same benefits as the beta-carotene found in whole foods; only whole foods innately possess the full range of optimum vitamins, minerals, antioxidants, phytochemicals, and dietary fiber that can increase an individuals' adaptive energies and improve their health.

THE EARTH, FOOD AND HEALTH

For a healthy body as well as a clear mind, it is very important to start with high quality ingredients and whole foods. Separating our physical health from the health of the environment, from which we eat our food, is not possible. Because we garner our nutrients from the health of the earth, the health of the soil, the health of the animals and plants we eat, our vitality and wellness is closely interrelated. If the soil, plants and animals are not cared for and nourished properly, then the quality of what we consume will be diminished. Consequently, the status of our health will be diminished.

Those who think they have no time for healthy eating will sooner or later have to find time for illness.

Modified from : Edward Stanley (1826-1893) from The Conduct of Life

In order to achieve optimal vitality, educate yourself and learn about how your foods were grown. I recommend that you focus on purchasing fresh and when afford-able, organic foods—those that are grown without the use of genetic modification, toxic pesticides, herbicides, fungicides, or chemical fertilizers. These contaminants diminish the nutrient levels in the soil and in turn affect your quality of your foods and your health.

When you buy organic, you back a sensi-ble farm policy that endorses farmers and also protects the wellness of all Americans. Organic foods are typically grown in a way that supports a healthy environment. They are usually free of pesticide and insecticide residues which are toxic to the body.

Just look at Mother Nature's most famous food, the apple. Most of us think of an apple as a healthy food staple. However, when it is sprayed with chemicals like chlo-rpyrifos, captan, iprodione, and vinclozolin, this is what happens:

Chlorpyrifos
Endocrine disruptor, impairs immune response, reproductive abnormalities, damages the developing nervous system and brain.

Captan
Carcinogenic, genetic and immune system damage.

Ipodione
Carcinogenic

Vinclozin
Carcinogenic, genetic endocrine and reproductive disruptor.[7]

In Washington State, a study of 110 urban and suburban children found that children who ate non-organic food had high levels of organophosphorus. Organophosphorus is a nervous system and immune disrup-tor, commonly caused by chemicals used in domestic and industrial settings like: insecticides, nerve gases, and herbicides. According to the U.S. Department of Health and Human Services, such orgno-phosphate pesticides (OP), are now found "in the blood of 95 percent of Americans tested [and] these levels are two times as high in adults as in children." Exposure to OP is connected to: hyperactivity, behavior disorders, learning disabilities, develop-mental delays, and motor dysfunction. The U.S. Center for Disease Control states that one of the major sources of toxic pesticide exposure in children, comes from the food they eat. Therefore, it was no surprise that the children who ate primarily organic foods had exposure levels below the EPA's safe level and that the only children to test negative for organophosphorus were on an all-organic diet.[8]

CHAPTER

two

food for thought

Are you familiar with the saying "Keep it Simple?" You know, those ideas and situations that are best handled in a straightforward manner. That way, no one is in doubt about what is being conveyed. Take this idea to the level of food. Clean, honest, uncomplicated whole foods. Nothing has been added, nothing taken away. You know what you are eating. Nourishment in its most pure form, it provides the building blocks for our bodies.

Clean proteins, healthy fats, and mineral rich complex carbohydrates, sustain growth, repair cells and furnish energy for all the activities of the body. This sustenance is needed to preserve the integrity of each cell of the body. It is the source necessary to create vital energy. Healing with simple whole foods profoundly affects all systems of the body.

Yet, in this age of excess, the practice of simple eating can be challenging. Over 50,000 different types of foods and food products are available in America from all around the world. Eating foods with at least a dozen ingredients in each meal is nothing short of a gastronomic disaster. Triggering both mental and digestive havoc in the body, complicated foods are a recipe for ill health. Instead, chart a new course and remember that the path to equilibrium in health is paved with simplicity.

And to help ensure your success on this new journey towards health, I have created this chapter as your mini-nutritional balancing food encyclopedia. With a concise, compilation of important information, this compendium will provide you with the foundation to begin building your health. I hope it will compel you to look twice and think twice the next time you shop for food.

NUTRITIONAL BUILDING BLOCKS

PROTEINS

Proteins are the most amazing group of molecules in the human body. They are composed from an incredible complex chain of smaller molecules called amino acids. They are the main building blocks of the body. Meats, poultry, fish, eggs, cheese, yogurt, soy and peanuts are considered 'complete proteins'. This is a useful but not absolutely true concept that means that these proteins contain a good balance of all of the essential amino acids that our bodies need. Our bodies require at least twenty-two amino acids for health and well-being. Of these, ten or so are called 'essential' because our bodies cannot make them. This means we need to ingest them in our diet. We don't need to eat the other twelve or so, because we can convert the essential ones into them inside our bodies.

STARCHES OR COMPLEX CARBOHYDRATES

Carbohydrates are "fuel" foods for our bodies. They are of two basic types:

Sugars

These are also called simple carbohydrates. They are quite simple molecules. Their names include glucose, fructose, maltose, sucrose and others. They are among the most basic of human foods. Sugars are the simplest type of carbohydrates. They are also called simple carbohydrates. Chemically, most are ring-shaped structures with five or six carbon atoms arranged in a circle or ring. This ring is under tension. When we eat sugars, our bodies are able to open the ring, releasing energy. This is somewhat like opening a jack-in-the-box. Opening the ring structure releases the energy, similar to releasing a spring that is under tension.

Starches

These are also called complex carbohydrates. They are made up of groups of sugars that are bound tightly together. Their structure is more complex, and during digestion they break down into sugars.

COMMON FOODS THAT ARE HIGH IN STARCHES:

Grains

Such as rice, corn, wheat, oats, barley, rye, millet, and others. This means that all breads, pastries, cookies, cakes, pasta, spaghetti, potato and corn chips, French fries, doughy foods, deep fried foods, noodles, and pie crusts tend to be very starchy foods.

Starchy Vegetables

Such as potatoes, sweet potatoes, yams, carrots, parsnips and to some degree onions.

Dried Beans

Such as pinto beans, lentils, garbanzo beans, black beans, navy beans, black-eyed peas, red beans, aduki beans and many others eaten around the world.

FATS AND OILS

Fats and oils are chains of molecules called fatty acids that are composed mainly of carbon atoms. Fats are generally solid at room temperature, while oils are liquid at room temperature. High-quality fats and oils are one of the most essential foods to consume every day. They are needed for your brain, for energy production and for making many vital hormones in the body. Fats do not drive up your insulin level, create insulin resistance and make you fat, as do sugar and carbohydrates. They also do not rob your body of minerals, as does eating sugars and many starches as well. Last but not least, fats and oils make our food taste good. Sources of high quality fats and oils are meats, fish, dairy products, nuts and seeds, vegetable oils, and a small amount of olive oil, coconut oil.

ORIENTAL PHILOSOPHY OF FOOD

YIN AND YANG—HOT AND COLD

All physical life and health depends on creating the correct balance between opposing and complementary forces that are traditionally called yin and yang. This philosophy lies at the foundation of Chinese culture. This selection of food choices comes from a comprehensive system regarding metabolic types. Yin and yang refer to specific qualities of life. Yang is more male, warm, contracted, and hot and yin is more female, expanded, and cool. For example, a hot dry desert climate is very yang, while a cool, damp one is more yin. Similarly, a healthy body should be slender, warm and athletic. This is a more yang condition, for both men and women. This system is used in nutritional balancing science since most everyone today is yin, necessitating a diet more abundant in yang foods.

Yin vs. Yang Foods

TABLE 2.1

YIN FOODS	YANG FOODS
Cooked beans	Salt
Raw vegetables	Eggs
Certain vegetables: *Nightshade family (tomatoes, potatoes, eggplant and all peppers) These include white potatoes, tomatoes, eggplant, okra, and all peppers, both sweet red and yellow and green ones and hot peppers*	Red meat
Fruit	Poultry
Fruit juice	Fish
Assorted powders such as protein powders, green drinks, and smoothies	Cooked root vegetables: *foods that grow below the ground*
Sugars	Other cooked vegetables
Alcohol	Grains such as millet and buckwheat
Drugs	

WHY IS THE IDEA OF YIN AND YANG SO IMPORTANT?

- *Health is more than just filling the body with nutrients and removing toxins. Most illness produces a colder, more expanded, much more yin body. Certain infections such as fungal ones are far more yin and cold than others such as bacterial infections that cause high fevers.*

- *A better yin-yang balance greatly increases adaptive energy, restores some enzyme systems and greatly increases the energy efficiency of the body.*

- *True fast oxidizers, of which there are few today, are much more yang.*

- *Today, many people are yin. The reasons for this include: poor overall health and fatigue, toxic metals in our bodies, negative attitudes, medicines and recreational drugs, electromagnetic fields from cell phones and computers and lastly, diets of refined foods.* [9]

Yin-Yang is one way to choose foods for the slow and fast oxidizer.

BASIC CONCEPTS OF YIN AND YANG

Nutritional balancing science finds that the macrobiotic classification of yin and yang foods is more accurate today than the traditional oriental medicine classification.

These types of food choices can be traced back thousands of years and includes the following: the basic characteristics involve a diet of kelp, sea salt, meats and especially cooked vegetables. It is important to try to avoid yin foods such as sugars, sweet juices, most fruit, nightshade vegetables (this includes, eggplant, tomatoes, peppers and potatoes as they are inflammatory) and most uncooked food. Food group choices are divided into foods that are more yin in nature, versus those that are more yang in nature.[10]

SPIRITUAL ASPECTS OF FOOD

Certain foods contain sufficient amounts of minerals, vitamins, or other substances that appear to assist people in the development of the finer brain centers. They are as follows:

Proteins
Includes sardines, lamb, eggs, Braga Farms pistachio nuts, (www.buyorganicnuts.com), a small amount of Brazil nuts, green lentils, and toasted almond butter.

Grains
Includes blue corn tortillas or blue corn tortilla chips, organic yellow corn or organic yellow corn chips. (Yellow corn products are not quite as good as the blue corn products, but are acceptable.)

Vegetables
Most cooked vegetables are superb with the exception of the nightshade family. A supplement of kelp is also excellent. And lastly, an excellent recommendation is Botija olives that are raw and dried.

IDEAL FOODS FOR THE NUTRITIONAL BALANCING PROGRAM

VEGETABLES: STAY LOCAL! BE CREATIVE.
The word for vegetable comes from the Latin word vegetare, meaning to grow, flourish or to bring life. Vegetables provide just that, a life force or energy to assist our well-being. Vegetables are wonderful. Packed with an assortment of vitamins, minerals and fiber, this diet recommends cooked vegetables cover at least half to two thirds of your plate twice a day. Or another way to look at this bountiful serving size of these prized foods is to double or triple your usual serving. However, one of the most pressing problems in today's diets is the lack of cooked vegetables. Getting 70 percent or more of your diet as cooked vegetables is often a challenge. Don't give up. These foods are in a class all their own. Experiment! Try as many different kinds of vegetables as you can.

A WORD ON NIGHTSHADES
Do your best to limit nightshade vegetables (tomatoes, potatoes, eggplants and all peppers). These vegetables can cause inflammatory side effects, such as triggering arthritis flare–ups in cases of osteoarthritis, rheumatoid arthritis, or other joint problems like gout. Nightshade vegetables are technically fruits and are more "yin" in Oriental terms. Mushrooms are also a food to use only occasionally because they are yin and are a fungus organism.

BROCCOLI

Broccoli deserves its reputation of being a celebrity in the nutrition world. It has well documented cancer-fighting abilities. Broccoli is responsible for its impact on your health because it contains in-dole-3-carbinol, a strong antioxidant and stimulator of detoxifying enzymes. It also seems to protect the structure of DNA and reduce the risk of breast and cervical cancer. Finally, broccoli growers tend to shy away from using pesticides due to the vegetables own use of a natural insect repellent. In 2003, the Environmental Working Group, a consumer advocate nonprofit research organization, put broccoli on its list of twelve foods least contaminated with pesticides. [11]

SWISS CHARD

Swiss Chard, is a diva in the vegetable world. This leafy green has only 35 calories in a cup and yet boasts:

- . Almost 4 grams of fiber
- More than 100 mg of calcium
- 961mg of potassium
- More than 30mg of vitamin C
- About 10,000 IU of Vitamin A
- 19,000 mcg of lutein and zexanthin, members of the carotenoid family that have strong antioxidant properties

Shipping is a terrible thing to do to vegetables. They probably get jet lagged, just like people.

Elizabeth Berry

CABBAGE

Cabbage has wonderful health benefits. Women living in Eastern European countries, where cabbage rates high as a staple vegetable, were less likely to develop breast cancer than women who lived in the United States.[12] Like broccoli, cabbage contains indoles, a property that can reduce the risk of cancer. However, you should be advised that all members of the cabbage family contain goitrogens, that when eaten raw, can suppress the function of the thyroid gland. These vegetables include cabbage, broccoli, rutabaga, cauliflower, kale, brussels sprouts and watercress. However, please note, cooking these vegetables breaks down the goitrogens, rendering them inactive.

SPINACH

Popeye's favorite, this leafy green nutrient dense food packs in the vitamins, minerals and various other phytonutrients. Readily available around the world, this superfood is easy to find in the market and has the added bonus of being affordable. Being a versatile food, it can be eaten in soups, steamed or sautéed. As you eat this food, remember that spinach has loads of antioxidants which protects the body from free radicals, those rogue molecules that damage tissues and cause illness. Maybe Popeye knew that when he squeezed those cans of spinach into his mouth, he was not only making himself strong, but also was protecting his body against various diseases.

TURNIPS, RUTABAGAS, PARSNIPS, CARROTS, BEETS, CELERY ROOT, ONIONS, GARLIC, RADISHES, YAMS & SWEET POTATOES

These unpopular vegetables should be far more celebrated. Turnips are one of those high-volume foods that can fill you up without adding lots of calories to your diet. Turnip greens, a great source of vitamins A and K, are terrific for bones. Parsnips are another healthy choice. This pale vegetable looks similar to a carrot, minus the bright orange color. They are sweet and they are a great alternative to the white potato. Please add these rooties to your shopping list. (I have included recipes herein to help you learn how to prepare these mysterious marvels.)

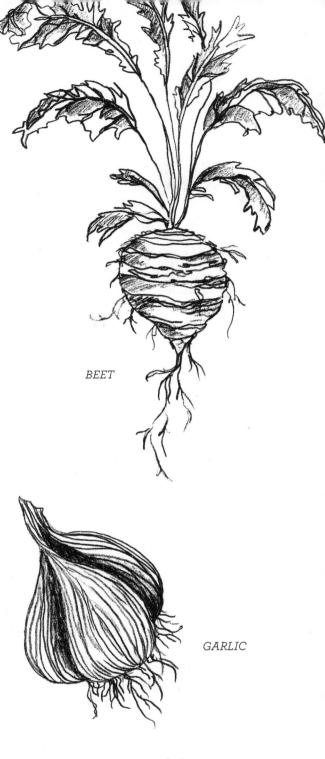

BEET

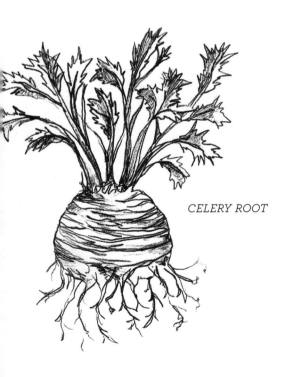

CELERY ROOT

GARLIC

Root Vegetables
(noun) Any of the various fleshy edible underground roots or tubers

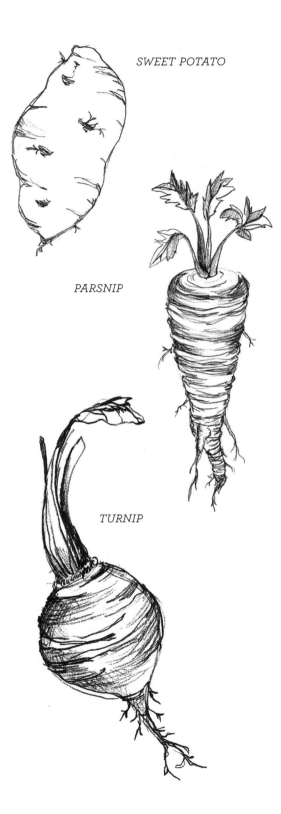

SWEET POTATO

PARSNIP

TURNIP

JUICING

Cellular cleansing. That is one of benefits of juicing. By oxygenating and cleansing the body, you create and enhance the health and fitness of your body from the inside out. Juicing your veggies, provides your body with a boost of nutrients, enzymes, vitamins and minerals in a form that the body can easily utilize, absorb and digest. Easily absorbed minerals such as calcium, potassium and silicon are contained within fresh juice. These minerals help the body to restore the biochemical and mineral balance in the cells. In addition, juicing concentrates the nutrients by eliminating the fibrous part of the raw vegetables and/or other foods that are juiced. Studies show that the nutrients from juiced vegetables are within your bloodstream within thirty minutes of consumption.

Unfortunately, juicing also has many of the problems of raw foods. For this reason, it is only recommend that you consume 10-12 ounces of carrot juice daily, perhaps with some greens added. One or two ounces of wheat grass juice are also excellent for most people and essential in some cases in which a person is very debilitated.

CAUTIONS REGARDING JUICING

Cleanliness
This is true with other raw foods as well. For example, never have carrot juice from a juice bar unless you are sure the carrots and other ingredients are thoroughly washed in very clean water and soap. Also, after juicing, the equipment must be washed well after every use, as it can harbor molds and bacteria. Otherwise, you could easily pick up parasites, bacteria or even worse from a glass of very fresh juice. Packaged or store-bought

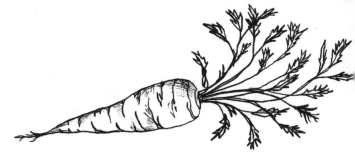

juice can have the same problems, and can easily become moldy if not consumed in a few days at the most.

Very, Very Yin
Juices are extremely yin products, even more so than other raw food because the food is broken up.

Too Much
Juice can be hard to digest, especially when taken with food. Some people drink a lot of vegetable or fruit juice. It is very high in sugar and overloads the system with certain nutrients. Therefore, always limit the amount and do not add sweeteners or fruit to vegetable juices.

Toxicity
Juices can concentrate toxic substances found in fruits and vegetables. This is often a hidden problem with juicing today, even when organic vegetables are used. It is hard to overcome. For example, pesticides may be concentrated in juices. Fiber in foods helps prevent absorption of some of these chemicals. To help prevent this, use only organic vegetables for juicing.

High Sugar
Juices with high sugar content, including even carrot juice to a degree, can upset the blood sugar level. Be careful with juicing if your blood sugar is unstable. As a solution, try to eat some, preferably, a fat and protein with the juice, or shortly after so help stabilize your blood sugar level. However, ideally juice should be taken without other food for about 15 minutes on either side of ingesting, to optimize absorption.

CARROT JUICE—"WHAT'S UP DOC?"
There is good reason that Bugs Bunny always ate his carrots. History shows that the carrot has been recorded as medicine by the early Greeks, and has since been valued by many different cultures. Carrot juice, the king of vegetable juice, is often referred to as the "miracle juice" because of its many health benefits. Research finds it provides protective agents in the building and maintenance of health in both young and old. It has a delicious sweet flavor that makes it very appealing to everyone, either plain or combined with other green vegetables.

This orange colored vegetable has one of the highest amounts of beta-carotenes as well as a cohort of other carotenes. It not only contains vitamins B, C, D, E and K; it also is mineral rich, with calcium, copper, magnesium, potassium, sodium, phosphorus, sulfur and iron. These alkaline minerals help soothe and tone the intestinal wall, as well as build bones and teeth. This protein and mineral rich juice also builds skin, hair and nails. Additionally, carrot juice has a tonic and cleansing effect on the liver, which helps to release bile and excess fats. The juice is also excellent because it provides a readily bio-available form of calcium. While it is difficult for the human body to absorb high levels of calcium from sources such as dairy, which are pasteurized and homogenized, the calcium in fresh carrot juice recipes is easily assimilated. (However, if the dairy you consume is certified raw dairy, then that is the best source of calcium.)

HOW TO GROW WHEATGRASS
A BEGINNER'S GUIDE

(See page 192 for instructions on juicing this nutrient rich grass)

1. Purchase wheat berries.

2. Soak around 1 cup of your wheat berries in water for about 12 hours.

3. Prepare a 20 x 10 inch seed tray with it being around 2 inches in depth. Add about 1½ inches of moist compost and potting mix.

4. After soaking, drain the seeds, rinse thoroughly and drain the seeds again.

5. Spread the seeds evenly over the compost mix. Add another half inch of soil. Add water and evenly distribute over the soil. Make sure to keep the soil moist and water the grass each day.

6. Cover the tray with moist newspaper to keep moisture surrounding the plant.

7. After three days, the wheatgrass should be a couple of inches in height.

8. Remove cover and place the wheatgrass tray where it will receive plenty of indirect sunlight. Direct sunlight can cause drying out of the soil, which inhibits growth.

Harvest when the grass is about seven inches tall as that is when it is at its nutritional peak.

HAVE A WHEATGRASS PARTY— THE POWER OF WHEATGRASS

In the Egyptian civilizations, dating back over 5000 years ago, wheatgrass, a cereal grass, was revered for its health qualities. Today, it is still thought by many to be a potent healer as it possesses a nutrient dense mineral profile and has many health benefits to boot. It is one of the "green foods" that are valued as a healing and restorative tonic.

Wheatgrass is grown from wheat berries and is harvested after just seven days of growth. Because wheatgrass is fibrous, it must be liquefied through the use of a juicer before it can be consumed. You can then drink wheatgrass juice either by itself or mix it with carrot juice. I recommend starting with only one ounce a day of wheatgrass juice because too much can cause nausea or stomach upset due to the strong cleansing effects of the juice.

Listed on the next page are some of the benefits of drinking this green juice.

- *Wheatgrass juice is one of the best sources of living chlorophyll available. It is high in oxygen like all green plants that contain chlorophyll. The brain and all body tissues function at an optimal level in a highly oxygenated environment.*

- *Chlorophyll is anti-bacterial and can be used inside and outside the body as a healer. Dr. Bernard Jensen believes that it only takes minutes to digest wheatgrass juice.*

- *It has been proven that chlorophyll arrests growth and development of unfriendly bacteria.*

- *Chlorophyll (wheatgrass) rebuilds the bloodstream. Studies of various animals have shown chlorophyll to be free of any toxic reaction. The red cell count was returned to normal within 4 to 5 days of the administration of chlorophyll, even in those animals which were known to be extremely anemic or low in red cell count.*

- *Liquid chlorophyll gets into the tissues, refines them and makes them over.*

- *Chlorophyll neutralizes toxins in the body.*

- *Chlorophyll helps purify the liver.*

- *Chlorophyll improves blood sugar problems.*

NOTE: Wheatgrass juice can be purchased in your local health food market in either the frozen section, or in a powder form.

SALADS

Moo! Cows have four stomachs and chew their cud. Human beings do not. Many people think that living on salad is good for their health. However, this is not true. The nutritional balancing program suggests that a little salad is ok as part of an overall diet, but should not be more than 5 percent of one's vegetable intake. I bet you're wondering why? Salads are not as nutrient rich as other vegetables (like cauliflower or broccoli) and therefore does not count as a vegetable. Additionally, there can be cleanliness issues, especially in restaurants, as salad can contain bacteria, parasites and other microorganisms from not being properly washed. So fill your plate with loads of cooked veggies and your body will thank you.

EGGS

This wonderful food is guaranteed to get your flock flying sunny side up. The inexpensive egg is probably nature's most perfect food and is best when eaten softly cooked. When preparing eggs at high heat, the structure of the nutrients can be damaged. Eggs should be cooked so that they are runny and loose. They are best eaten soft with the yolks runny. Because the yolk is a fat, it is best eaten raw or very lightly cooked. Additionally, it is not recommended that you eat eggs hard-boiled because it makes the protein very difficult to digest. Excellent ways to cook eggs are poaching, soft boiling, soft-scrambled or even fried over easy but not overcooked so the egg is rubbery.

Free range and organic eggs are best. Local eggs are a good choice as well.

FREE RANGE EGGS

These hens can roam freely on pasture and forage for their own food. These eggs are packed with more vitamins, Omega-3 fatty acids and less cholesterol.

ORGANIC EGGS

These eggs are something to crow about. Hens that spend time on the pasture get exercise, fresh air and produce healthier eggs. They have excellent nutritional benefits. Eggs are loaded with vitamins and nutrients that help your eyes, brain, and heart because they contain choline, an organic compound that promotes cardio-vascular health and brain development. On the three of four scientific scales for protein quality used in the past few decades—Protein Efficiency Rating, Biological Value and Net Protein Utilization—eggs consistently score the highest in the quality of their protein. The egg came in first, ahead of milk, beef, whey and soy. If you would like to get the most health benefits from this practically perfect food, please eat the entire egg (excluding the shell of course) as both the egg white and the egg yolk are good for you. And that's no yolk.

NOTE: Eggshells can be placed in the soil of your garden to grow flowers and vegetables. They enrich the soil with calcium to create beautiful blossoms.

HINT ON COOKING MEATS

Meats should be lightly cooked, just enough to kill all surface bacteria and parasites, and cooked through enough to kill most germs in the meat itself. Do not overcook meats.

MEATS

Excellent choices of meats are poultry, lamb, wild game, and moderate amounts of beef. (See Appendix G for a list of organizations that sell quality meats.) What is the difference between grass fed meats, organic, natural and free range?

GRASS FED MEATS

Grass fed meat is defined as cattle that have been allowed to graze on a natural pasture and are not fed soy, grain or other growth promoting additives. Grass fed meat is a better choice than organic or natural. Cattle that are fed grass enhance their Omega-3 content by 60 percent.[13]

ORGANIC MEAT

Organic meat is free of unwanted chemicals and the animals are fed organic grains. These animals are raised without antibiotics or hormones. Although healthy, this meat is still nutritionally inferior to grass fed meat.

NATURALLY RAISED MEATS & POULTRY

These types of meats are products that have no additives or hormones.

FREE RANGE

Free range meats come from animals that are allowed to roam freely on pasture. It is important to note, when an animal is taken off of a grass pasture and fattened on any type of grain (ordinary, genetically modified, or organic grain), it loses a number of valuable nutrients. Compared to grass fed meat, grain fed meat has one quarter less of vitamin E, one eighth less beta-carotene and lacks as much as one third of anti-inflammatory omega-three fatty acids. This is simply due to the fact that grains have fewer nutrients than grass.[14]

SARDINES

This tiny fish is a giant in the nutritional world. Look at its benefits:

* Low in mercury

* High in Omega-3 fatty acids

* High in amounts of D3

* High in RNA and DNA

* Rich source of bio-available calcium

* Great source of selenium

* Low calorie snack or super-nutritious meal

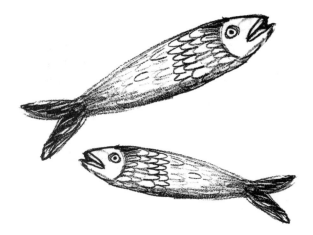

FISH

Fish is one of the best sources of protein and healthy fats. However, it is also one of the most concentrated sources for toxins, such as mercury. *(See Appendix C for information on Toxic Metals.)* The sewage and industrial waste dumped into the oceans by countries all over the world has altered the health benefits of seafood. Though fish is a great source of protein, and offers excellent fats and vitamins, I would recommend limiting it to only once a month, except for sardines and other small fish. Stay away from the "big kahuna" fish such as swordfish, shark, tuna and other large deepwater fish. These fish tend to have more mercury than the smaller fish, as they are higher up in the food chain and consume more toxins through a diet of other predatory fish.

Some farm-raised fish also have drawbacks. However, shop around and learn which options are the healthiest. There are some farms that raise their fish in the same manner as commercial cattle feeding them grains, soy and antibiotics.

When you want to put salmon on the menu, try to choose wild salmon. Wild salmon subsist on a diet of krill and shrimp. Krill and shrimp contain astaxanthin, a member of the carotenoid family. This accounts for wild salmon's intense pink pigment.

Because they are lower on the feeding chain, smaller fish are safest to consume and contain less mercury. Sardines are a convenient and health-boosting choice. They are loaded with Omega-3, calcium, iron, magnesium, phosphorus, potassium, zinc, copper, manganese, as well as B vitamins.

NOTE: Wild Salmon is only recommended once a month due to high mercury content. Also know that the FDA is debating whether to allow salmon to become a genetically modified food. Stay up to date and follow this food's future.

PORK (PIG PRODUCTS)

NOTE: Although pork is a protein, it is not recommended other than in this one particular form, porcine pancreatin.

Pork is not part of the nutritional balancing program because it may contain parasites, cysts or eggs. If eating pork infected with these uninvited guests, you can experience a multitude of symptoms ranging from nausea and diarrhea to muscle pains and headaches. In some cases, it has been reported that patients have difficulty coordinating movements and have difficulty breathing.

DAIRY

Nutritional balancing recommends pure, raw, (raw milk is milk from cows, sheep, or goats that has not been pasteurized to kill harmful bacteria) certified dairy products as excellent sources of Omega-3 fatty acids, calcium, magnesium, vitamins such as A and D, and many other nutrients. These foods should not be eaten in excess, but a glass of raw milk or raw cheese or raw yogurt can be an excellent addition to most people's diets.

WHAT IS CERTIFIED RAW DAIRY?

A certified raw dairy product means that the animals and equipment have been rigorously inspected and tested for bacteria as this food has not been pasteurized. The process of pasteurization destroys vital enzymes, diminishes vitamin content, denatures fragile milk proteins, destroys vitamins C, B12 and B6, kills beneficial bacteria, promotes pathogens and is associated with allergies, increased tooth decay, colic in infants, growth problems in children, osteoporosis, arthritis, heart disease and cancer.

THE BENEFITS OF RAW MILK

Besides the incredible, rich taste of raw milk products, raw milk is a super food for most people. Unlike pasteurized milk, raw milk provides the following benefits:

- *It is full of beneficial gut bacteria that are vital for optimum digestion and immunity.*

- *Raw milk has the full spectrum of amino acids and is a complete protein.*

- *Real raw milk–full-fat, unprocessed milk from pasture-fed cows–contains vital nutrients like fat-soluble vitamins A and D, calcium, vitamin B6, B12, and CLA. (conjugated linoleic acid, a fatty acid naturally occurring in grass-fed beef and milk that reduces body fat and protects against cancer.)*

- *It boasts numerous nutrients packed with folic acid, B vitamins, vitamin C, Omega-3 fatty acids and other nutrients that are mostly or completely destroyed in pasteurization.*

- *It offers a perfect balance of minerals such as calcium and magnesium.*

- *Raw milk also has many live enzymes necessary for digesting food and enjoying good health.*

- *It also contains compounds that combat arthritis, cholesterol, and arterial stiffening.*

Remember: All Fats Are Not Created Equal!

Furthermore, statistics show that children growing up on farms are less likely to develop allergies. In a study at the University of London, children were given two glasses of raw milk a week. Their incidence of developing hay fever was cut by 10 percent and eczema by 38 percent. In 2009, a Swiss study of nearly 15,000 European children showed that those who drank raw milk had lower rates of asthma and allergies.

Generally, most people have found when consuming raw milk products, that health improvements naturally occur. For instance, many people report clearer skin, better digestion, increased respiratory function, boosted immunity, fewer allergies and improved energy and overall health.

PASTEURIZING MILK
Pasteurization, where milk is heated for short periods followed by rapid cooling, destroys the nutritional content of milk. Pasteurization dismantles lactase, an enzyme that helps digest the milk-sugar lactose, meaning that lactose-intolerant individuals can drink raw milk but not pasteurized milk. This process also renders calcium more difficult for the body to absorb. Today, milk may even be ultra-pasteurized, where it is heated at higher temperatures for even longer periods of time. The industry says this is necessary due to heat resistant organisms that might pass traditional pasteurization. Moreover, ultrapasteurization gives milk a longer shelf life—up to four weeks.

WHERE TO FIND RAW MILK?
Presently, there are only eight states that allow raw milk to be sold in stores for human consumption—Arizona, California, Connecticut, Maine, Pennsylvania, South Carolina, New Mexico and Washington. In Florida, you can get around the law as long as the milk is marked as pet food. In some of the many states where purchasing raw milk is illegal, you can cow share and actually buy your own cow. I recommend that you visit realmilk.com for additional information on where you can purchase raw milk. Another new trend is "milk clubs," where folks take turns driving to farms to purchase milk for everyone else. So what is one to do? Before purchasing raw milk products, get to know your farmer. Ask questions, such as are the cows mostly on pasture? Are the animals and barn kept clean? And once the cows are milked, is the milk transferred to stainless steel tanks or clean containers where it is kept chilled? After that the milk should be used within a week as it will begin to sour. (though it is not dangerous when it does so.) With all of these suggestions, give this raw moo juice a try. It is a healthy, safe and nutritious food.

THE SKINNY ON FATS...
There is much confusion that surrounds the subject of fats. Unhealthy fats and refined foods can lead to mineral deficiencies. These foods are anti-nutrients and compete in the absorption of vitamins and minerals. In the absence of nutrient-rich foods, those that are loaded with vitamins and minerals, blood vessel walls tend to weaken.[15] Instead, pack your plate with nutrient dense foods such as vegetables, healthy proteins (such as chicken and lamb) and healthy fats.

Healthy fats are a critical part of this diet. Oils and fats not only carry flavor, they provide us with energy. Fats play an integral role in building and repairing cell membranes. Fats protect the vital organs from trauma and environmental changes by padding and insulating our body. They also aid in the production and balance of hormones and hormone-like substances. They act as carriers for fat-soluble vitamins such as A, D, E, and K.[16] Fats help us to feel "full," reducing cravings for in-between-meal snacks.

Recommended fats for this diet are: butter, eggs, quality meats like lamb, turkey and chicken, flax oil, hemp oil, cod liver oil and a variety of nut butters, and a small amount of olive oil, coconut oil. Allowed in reduced amounts are peanut, safflower, sunflower, sesame and corn oil.

It is best to avoid all hydrogenated oils, (margarines, shortening, commercial peanut butter), and trans-fats, (oil used for commercial deep frying, cake mixes, fast foods, many frozen foods, most packaged cookies and crackers, non-dairy creamers, non-dairy whipped topping as well as margarine.) You will often find the words, "hydrogenated," or "partially hydrogenated oil," on many packages of processed foods and most snack foods. These oils promote heart disease, cancer, diabetes,

As for butter versus margarine, I trust cows more than chemists.

Joan Gussow

immune dysfunction and obesity. Additionally, trans-fats increase the bad LDL cholesterol, triglycerides and insulin levels and reduce the good HDL cholesterol.

ESSENTIAL FATTY ACIDS

If we are to understand the value of a healthy diet without trying to understand healthy fats, than we will be unable to appreciate the value of Omega-3's. The royalty in the world of fats is appropriately referred to as the Queen of Fats. The Omega-3's are some of the most vital and essential nutrients in the support of human health. Enormously important in the composition of every cell, these fats help to determine how well your cell works as part of your ultimate health.

These Omega-3's are loaded with Essential Fatty Acids, (EFA's) and are concentrated in only a few tissues of the body, especially the brain. The brain is the organ that has the highest percentage of fat found in the human body.[17] An interesting fact to know is that 20 percent of the dry weight of the brain is made up of EFA/DHA.[18] EFA's are not only a critical part of your brain, but also part of your inner ear, eyes, adrenal glands and sex organs. EFA's are not made in the body so they must be eaten to obtain them.

EFA'S ARE IMPORTANT BECAUSE THEY:

- *Repair and produce cell membranes.*

- *Produce hormones that can help maintain heart rate, blood clotting and reduce inflammation.*

- *Obtain needed nutrition and dispose of harmful wasted products.*

A WORD ON HEMP OIL

This oil does not contain THC, the active psychotropic agent in cannabis or marijuana. An amazing food source, hempseed is 25 percent protein and is a high-quality, nutritionally complete food. Hempseed oil has the highest concentration of essential fatty acids of any oil (about 80 percent). The hemp plant acts as an antibacterial, antiviral, anticonvulsant, bronchodilator and expectorant. It reduces spasticity and ataxia in multiple sclerosis, stops menstrual bleeding and helps PMS and the pain of childbirth.

- *Necessary for nerve transmission*

- *Aid in fighting infections*

- *Assist in proper growth in children*

- *Lack or imbalance of this fat is linked to Heart attacks, Cancer, Depression, Lupus, Asthma, Obesity, ADHD and Alzheimer's*

WHAT FOODS CONTAIN THE MOST OMEGA-3's?

- *Sardines, anchovies, salmon*

- *Raw milk products, organic milk products*

- *Lamb*

- *Wild game*

- *Grass fed animals*

- *Eggs from grass fed chickens*

- *Flax oil, *hemp oil*

- *Small amounts in walnuts, pumpkin seeds, brazil nuts, sesame seeds*

NUT BUTTERS AND SPREADS
Recommended are small quantities of nuts, nut butters and seeds.

ALMOND BUTTER
A small amount of almond butter is a terrific nutritional treat, a great alternative to peanut butter. Unfortunately, peanut butter can contain molds and can cause food sensitivities for some people. (Some peanuts and peanut butter can contain aflatoxins. According to the USDA, this mold is a cancer-causing poison produced by certain fungi.)

It is important to note that almonds contain good fats that lower bad cholesterol and are a great source of vitamin E, magnesium and potassium.

YOU CAN MAKE GREAT MILK WITH ALMONDS.

Add a handful of almonds to 1-2 cups of spring water and mix in the blender. This is terrific by itself or with some stevia for those of you who have a sweet tooth!

CASHEW BUTTER

A small amount of cashew butter is particularly delicious and is often found in Indian dishes and curries. Give these nuts a try when cooking dishes with an Indian flare. This nut butter is also heart healthy by lowering LDL's. Low Density Lipoproteins (the bad cholesterol and raising the protective HDL's, High Density Lipoprotein (the good cholesterol) Cashews are high in magnesium, calcium, phosphorus, potassium, copper and selenium.

SEED BUTTERS

A small amount of sunflower butter and sesame butter/tahini are high in protein, nutrients and unsaturated fats. They are low in saturated fats, and of course, they contain no cholesterol or trans-fatty acids. In addition, they are important allies in decreasing the risk of heart disease. Sunflower seed butter is a "powerhouse" of vitamins and minerals, including selenium, zinc, potassium, iron and protein!

"OPEN SESAME!"

The famous phrase, from the movie Arabian Nights, "open sesame reflects the unique feature of the sesame seed pod, which bursts open when it reaches maturity. Sesame butter, also known as tahini, is a rich source of minerals and B vitamins as well as an important amino acid, methionine. This amino acid aids in liver detoxification and helps with the absorption of other amino acids. Tahini is also a rich source of calcium, protein and B vitamins as well as EFA's (essential fatty acids) EFA's help maintain healthy skin. A versatile spread, tahini is delicious on vegetables, meats or even on an apple.

WATER

Water is magical. It nourishes and heals the human body. Every civilization started near a body of water. Water's role is vital to our health. In addition to being the best choice of beverage, it is vital for our bodies to have water. Water permits the human body to acquire essential nutrition as well as assist with elimination. Recommended are both distilled and spring waters. Carbon filtered water is second option for those who are watching their pennies, or are inconvenienced by carrying large containers of water into their home.

Statistics have shown that it comprises about 75 percent of our body. Water maintains equilibrium both inside and around the cells. This permits the body to absorb essential nutrients as well as eliminate waste.

TAP WATER

As valuable as water is, much of our water is not clean enough to drink. Sadly, it consists of chemicals and toxins. Tap water today, contains toxic metals and chemicals such as fluoride, lead, manganese and even medical drugs. It is best to avoid tap water, and drink bottled spring water or distilled water.

DISTILLED WATER

This water has no minerals and can assist the body in removing some of the metals that are loosely held in the tissues. It is only recommended for some people and for a period of only three months because it contains no trace minerals.

SPRING WATER

For daily drinking on a long-term basis, high quality spring water is recommended. It supplies many needed minerals, has been filtered through the earth to remove most toxins and microorganisms, and has not been damaged by processing. This type of water has a variety of minerals that can nourish the cells.

NOTE: *Find a hot or cold spring near your home where you can fill up your own bottles of water-plastic or glass—directly from a fresh spring. Visit the website: http://www.findaspring.com*

RECOMMENDED AMOUNTS OF WATER:

- *In general, an adult needs about three quarts of water per day. One suggestion to make sure you take in enough water everyday, is to keep a pitcher of water or a water bottle by your office desk, or with you in the car. Try infusing your water with cucumber, mint of even make mild teas like chamomile. You might find that you drink more water if it is kept within arms reach.*

- *Another suggestion to help you get your water intake each day is to begin your morning by drinking many glasses of water upon arising in the morning. This will keep your body supported for hours and you will not have to think about how much water to drink throughout the day.*

There are various types of filtration systems available as well. These include both Carbon Filtration and Reverse Osmosis.

HOUSEHOLD CARBON FILTERS

This type of water is an excellent second option of drinking water.

While this is a good option for some people, here are the problems to beware of with this type of system:

- *Carbon filters will not filter out fluoride, most toxic metals, certain small organic and other chemical contaminants.*

- *All carbon filters clog up in time and a dirty carbon filter is worse than no filter at all. Toxic metal testing in water samples have shown to be higher in filtered water than in tap water due to a dirty or clogged filter.*

REVERSE OSMOSIS

Nutritional balancing science does not recommend any reverse osmosis water. This method involves passing water at high pressure though a plastic membrane with tiny holes in it. Most substances are too large to pass through the membrane and remain behind. Below are common problems with reverse osmosis:

- *Appears to damage the water.*

- *It does not hydrate the body well.*

- *It is "Yin."*

- *Expensive to maintain as only 20 percent of the water passes through the membrane. (The rest is discarded as wastewater)*

- *Residue from the plastics affects the quality of the water.*

- *Reverse osmosis and deionization are used in most commercial "drinking water."*

For example, water stores, supermarket machines and bottling plants for soda pop, juices, beer and many other drinks (it is much cheaper than distillation) use this type of processing.

SPICES

HOW TO SPICE IT UP!

When we follow any dietary regimen we run the risk of cornering ourselves into a boring eating routine, cooking the same ingredients the same way time after time. This is easy to avoid by using different combinations of seasonings when you cook. Ingredients take on new life when combined with spices from other parts of the world. Herbs and spices can add some pizzazz even to the simplest dish. Seasonings are meant to enhance flavor, not overwhelm the ingredients you use.

The following reference guide is arranged according to the cuisines of different countries. According to Elisabeth Rozin, the late food expert, "every culture tends to combine a small number of flavoring ingredients so frequently and so consistently that they become definitive of that particular cuisine." You could easily define an entire culture by using two or three key flavorings. On the next few pages you will find spices arranged by culture. Select the spices that will best suit your taste for the type of meal you're preparing. Experiment! Sprinkle some cumin on broiled meat, or some lemongrass tossed into steamed vegetables. Adding new additions to your meals will give dishes zest. Herbs and spices have wonderful health benefits, too!

GROW A KITCHEN GARDEN

If you can purchase or grow your own herbs, you'll enjoy far better aromas and flavors. (When buying herbs, be sure the labels say" non-irradiated" in order to receive health benefits.) A kitchen garden can also be great fun for the kids. You can try growing basil, chives, rosemary and thyme. Some are of these herbs can be purchased in small windowsill pots as a way to make this new adventure easier. Remember that fresh herbs are best.

If you're successful with your herbs and have some to store, you can chop and blend them into sweet butter, place in an ice-cube tray, and store them for quick, flavorful additions when you cook. Another suggestion is to use an ice cube tray and when sauces are frozen, you can pop the ice cubes out and place them in Glad® zip top bags. This brand of zip tops does not release chemicals into your frozen items. You can always use these butters and sauces on your simple meals. This is particularly helpful if you have no time to spare for your meal preparation.

WHAT IS A SPICE?

A spice is "any dried, fragrant, aromatic or pungent vegetable or plant substance, in the whole, broken or ground form, that contributes to flavor, whose primary function in food is seasoning rather than nutrition, and that may contribute relish or piquancy to foods or beverages."

SPICES OF THE WORLD

& OTHER INTERESTING FACTS

mexican

CUMIN
Used in a variety of Mexican dishes. It is a great spice to prevent and relieve gas. Use it to cook beans. It is also a great way to spice up deviled eggs, and cottage cheese. Cumin is great on meat and can be a terrific marinade for shish-kebobs.

CILANTRO
A warm and spicy herb. It is great at easing digestion and nausea.

CAYENNE
Helps blood circulation and clotting.

GARLIC
A wonderfully rich tasting accent. Health benefits include building immunity and reducing blood pressure. Garlic is best finely chopped before adding toward the end of a sauté. Avoid burning garlic!

thai

LEMONGRASS
Has a refreshing citrus aroma and is used in coconut curries, beef and vegetable dishes. It can also help detoxify the liver.

CORIANDER
Great for aiding digestion.

TURMERIC
Adds color to your dish as well as an earthy, peppery flavor.

indian

CUMIN
Used to make Indian curry dishes. It has a full-bodied aroma.

TURMERIC
Adds a bit of yellow color to your dish. It's flavor is earthy and somewhat peppery. It has been known to help liver problems, enhance circulation and assist in digestion.

CORIANDER
Another main ingredient used in Indian dishes. It is known to aid digestion, diarrhea and nausea.

SAFFRON
Adds a beautiful yellow color and flavor to rice.

GARLIC
Great to sprinkle on your vegetables or to use as condiment as you cook meat. Garlic is a renowned cure in all cultures. It has been known to be a natural antibiotic and is used for lung ailments, colds, flus, fevers and earaches.

chinese

GINGER ROOT
Spicy and peppery, used in Asian dishes. It adds a refreshing flavor to marinades and stir-fries. Ginger is beneficial to the stomach and circulation. It has also been said to relieve morning sickness.

CAYENNE
Adds both heat and color to dishes. It is known to improve blood circulation and help blood to clot.

SOY SAUCE
Has a salty taste and is an excellent addition to Chinese dishes.

Do not cook with soy sauce; it is better to put it directly on your food when it is done cooking. Tamari is the best soy sauce to use. Try to purchase a brand without preservatives.

GARLIC
Great to sprinkle on your vegetables or to use as condiment as you cook meat. Garlic is a renowned cure in all cultures. It has been known to be a natural antibiotic and is used for lung ailments, colds, flus, fevers and earaches.

italian

BASIL
Has a delicate aroma. It can be added to eggs, broiled fish or chicken dishes. Basil helps to remedy indigestion, fever, colds and flu.

OREGANO
Has a robust flavor and is great on poultry dishes. It is known for relieving digestive problems.

THYME
Has a very strong flavor. It makes a great addition to soups and stews. Use it on meat and poultry.

GARLIC
Great to sprinkle on your vegetables or to use as condiment as you cook meat. Garlic is a renowned cure in all cultures. It has been known to be a natural antibiotic and is used for lung ailments, colds, flus, fevers and earaches.

french

DILL
Has a mild flavor. It is great on fish and in dips.

ROSEMARY
Can be added to your meats. Rosemary smells wonderful and is usually used on meat dishes. As a health benefit, rosemary is helpful in aiding headaches, indigestion and with respiratory problems.

TARRAGON
Has a warm flavor. It goes well with egg and cheese recipes. Known to relieve indigestion and promote sleep.

eastern european

PAPRIKA
Great on deviled eggs and on meats. If you purchase an excellent quality Hungarian paprika, you will get more flavor than color.

POPPY SEEDS
Can be used in a creative soup or in a salad dressing.

CARAWAY
A spiky seed that can be used on vegetables or with brown rice noodles. It helps with digestion and certain nervous conditions.

SEA SALT

Salt's major role in the body is to maintain cellular homeostasis. Traditional table salt is refined and may contain, aluminum, which is linked to heavy metal toxicity. Sugar, such as dextrose, has been used to preserve salt and stop it from changing color.

The right choice for your kitchen is unprocessed sea salt. Formed from the natural evaporation of ocean water, generally in man-made pools near a protected shoreline, this higher quality sea salts boasts up to 80 trace minerals.

Most of us are familiar with the macro-minerals such as calcium, magnesium, potassium and sodium. These minerals are needed in significant amounts by the body. Just as important, but needed in smaller amounts, are trace minerals. Some minerals contained in the preferred sea salts are boron, copper, manganese, nickel and selenium.

Because our food supplies do not contain the same levels of minerals as they once did, using sea salt is one way to help integrate these important nutrients into your body. For example, since the mid-1960's, there has been a decline in the levels of vitamins and minerals contained in our produce and meats. Today, broccoli has only 50 percent of the calcium it did in 1963. Over this same period of time, potassium levels in beets has dropped by 10 percent and spinach has 10 percent less magnesium.

HOW DO YOU LOOK FOR A QUALITY SEA SALT?
Choose a sea salt that is pollution free and harvested from ancient rock salt beds under remote mountainous regions of the world. For example, try buying Hawaiian jade sea salt or other quality sea salt from the Andes, Himalayas or Rockies.

The issue of getting enough trace minerals into our diet is important. Sprinkle some sea salt onto your food and enhance your body's overall health.

Salt is a bacteriostatic; it inhibits growth or multiplication of bacteria, by interfering with bacterial protein production, and it acts as a cleansing agent, removing dirt and dead skin cells.

STEVIA

Stevia rebaudiana, is a small plant that grows in South America. With three-hundred times the sweetness of sugar, yet virtually calorie free, this herb is on its way to becoming the natural sweetener of the future. If you use this product, use it sparingly.

NOTE: Stevia's sweet flavor is not affected by heat, and can be used in teas or other beverages or baked items. This product is available in powder or liquid. If using this product in the powder form, please know that one teaspoon of stevia is equal in sweetness to one cup of sugar. In the liquid form, 1/33 of a teaspoon is equal in sweetness to 1 teaspoon of sugar.

GRAINS

For thousands of years, grains have been grown around the world. Whole grains offer complex carbohydrates, protein, vitamins and minerals. The grains that are recommended as part of this regimen include, brown rice, buckwheat, quinoa, millet, corn and basmati rice.

COOKING HINT: Whole grains such as rice, millet, oats, rye, and quinoa should be cooked thoroughly so they are soft and easily eaten. In a few cases, they may also be sprouted and eaten as vegetables.

PROBLEM FOODS

WHEAT

Wheat is not part of this nutritional balancing program. Wheat, our most popular grain, has been hybridized[19] and inbred for production. As a result, it lacks nutritional value and is considered an "allergic" food. Problems with wheat are as follows:

- **Wheat is inbred for production.** *Even organic wheat, which is still a hybrid, contains very little useful chromium, zinc, manganese, selenium and other trace minerals. It is simply not a quality food any more.*

- **White bread has been stripped of the bran and fiber that contains small amounts of vital trace elements.** *This makes the bread or other flour products even more deficient in essential nutrients.*

- **Iron added to the flour by law in America, competes with chromium and other vital minerals.** *This negates any benefit from the small amount of chromium in the bread. In fact, it could negate the benefit* of all the chromium in the rest of the meal with which bread is eaten.

- **Hybridized wheat in any form, especially with added iron in an organic form, is very hard on digestion.** *This slowly weakens the digestive system and causes leaky gut, digestive enzyme deficiencies and other intestinal problems. This tends to worsen the absorption of all the essential elements in the diet.*

- **Most bread products, especially cakes, pastries, cookies and other prepared foods, have added sugar.** *Sugar directly interferes with chromium usage, as well as zinc, selenium and other. Sugar also forces the pancreas to work harder to metabolize the sugar, worsening glucose metabolism problems that are already made worse by the flour itself.*

- **Dozens of chemical additives used in most breads, cakes, pastries and other flour products are toxic, especially for the sensitive digestive tracts of children.** *This just further ruins digestion and creates more mineral deficiencies and intestinal disease.*

- **Bromide is required by law or baked products in American.** *Bromide interferes with iodine in the food, competing with it for absorption and utilization. This is one reason for the large number of hypothyroid problems in America and any nation that eats this chemical found in all breads, pastries and many other wheat products.*

- **Iodine is needed in every cell to prevent cancer and has many other functions.** *Low iodine[20], similar to low zinc lowers intelligence, influences behavior, causes*

depression, fatigue as well as many more serious problems.

- **Unwise laws also allows and even encourages bleaching of flour with chlorine containing bleaches.** *These have many damaging effects. Chlorine is one of the most harmful elements, unless it is in the form of salt.*

- **Chlorides compete with iodine causing iodine deficiency in practically the entire American population.** *Chlorine residue in the flour turns extremely toxic when baked, forming various chlorinated compounds that are similar to pesticide called chlorinated hydrocarbons. These are among the most toxic products known to mankind.[21]*

FRUITS

Vegetables, not fruits, are the valedictorian of the nutritional balancing program. Fruits such as berries or an apple should be minimally consumed.

The reasons fruits are limited are:

- *Fruits are yin*

- *Fruits are often hybridized*

- *Fruits upset blood sugar*

- *Fruit can cause Candida problems. We all live with microbes on our skin and body. Normally they do not cause health issues. Candida Albicans is yeast that lives in our mouth, throat, digestive tract, intestines, and genitourinary tract and is usually part of the normal bowel tract. However, when the immune system weakens, the balance of good and bad bacteria can become unbalanced and Candida growth can proceed to flourish.*

When good health is present, the immune system can keep the Candida from growing and spreading. Take care of your body, watch your diet and keep sugars to a minimum.

SUGAR

Refined white sugar is not part of this nutritional program. Eating white sugar has harmed the health of everyone who uses it. This product has also cost America, in particular, billions in health care costs, disability and loss of life. Some authorities have called it white poison. Refined sugar is harmful because it has no nutritional value, vitamins or minerals. Furthermore, the body is left with only pure, refined carbohydrates, which it cannot utilize effectively. A diet that is high in refined sugar can also result in unbalanced blood sugar, triggering a release of powerful stress hormones. The constant hormonal roller coaster caused by consuming sugary–junk foods overworks the adrenal glands, disturbing the hormonal balance.[22,23,24]

An overabundance of sugary products will eventually lead to various health conditions such as: degenerative diseases, allergies, obesity, alcoholism, drug addiction, depression and behavior problems. Refined sugar can also contribute to yeast infections, upset calcium metabolism and cause deficiencies in magnesium, zinc, manganese, chromium and B complex vitamins.[25]

Be careful to check your products as sugar is hidden in many foods. Labels list their ingredients by weight, and any product that has more sugar in it than other ingredients should not be consumed—plainly said, it is just too much sugar. This is important—the first four ingredients on a label should never include: sugar, dextrose, glucose, sucrose, corn syrup, fructose, honey, fruit juice, rice syrup, malt sweetener or evaporated cane juice. For example, these products contain hidden sugar:

- *Canned fruit*

- *Sweetened teas*

- *Salad dressing*

- *Bread*

- *Ketchup*

Also avoid all foods in which one of the first two ingredients are barley malt, brown sugar, buttered syrup, cane-juice crystals, cane sugar, caramel, carob syrup, chocolate, corn sweetener, corn syrup, date sugar, dextran, dextrose, diastatic malt, ethyl maltol, fructose, fruit juice, fruit juice concentrate glucose, glucose solids, golden sugar, golden syrup, grape sugar, high-fructose corn syrup, honey, invert sugar, lactose, malt sweetener, malt syrup, raw sugar, refiner's syrup, rice syrup, rice bran syrup, sorbitol, sorghum, syrup, sucrose, turbinado sugar, xylitol or yellow sugar. Agave syrup and molasses are a little better, but should also be limited.

"SOY VEY!"

Often touted as the miracle food and considered a staple in the vegetarian diet, soy is actually surrounded by a great deal of controversy. You might be wondering, what about the Asian diet? Traditionally fermented soy products like tempeh, miso or tofu are ok to eat but only occasionally. In fact, Asian diets do not contain large quantities of soy but have an abundance of vegetables and fish. In America, there is an abundance of soy food choices, most of which are cheap junk foods. Soy powders and soy isolates are leftover products from the manufacture of soy oil and contain chemical residues used in the oil extraction process. Soy chips, soymilk, soy ice cream, soy burgers, soy cheese, and soy lattes are poor food choices. There are many issues surrounding soy. Some of these problems are:

- *Soy contains toxins or anti-nutrients. One of these enzymes inhibits the action of enzymes for digestion.[26] In soy, there are also high levels of phytic acid, which reduces the absorption of calcium, magnesium, copper, iron and zinc.*

- *Soybeans contain a clot promoting substance that causes red blood cells to clump together and suppress thyroid function. It is called haemagglutinin. [27]*

- *Soy phytoestrogens can disrupt endocrine function, and possibly cause thyroid cancer.*

- *Recently the FDA has taken to reviewing its policy on soy health claims. Harvard Women's Health Watch in April 2006, titled an article called " Soy: Not so miraculous."*

PROTEIN DRINKS & SMOOTHIES

These products are not recommended as part of the nutritional balancing program because many of these powders contain combinations of dried milk powder, sugar, and chemical flavors that can be toxic or poor quality. These products are yin and not helpful in balancing the body's chemistry.

NOTE: If you are caught in a pinch and time is limited, please use only quality whey protein isolate powder that contains as little sugar or fruit as possible as these ingredients unbalance the body chemistry.

ENERGY BARS

Most energy bars have more sugar and unhealthy fats than a typical candy bar. Additionally they are low in fiber and nutritional value, with a scant serving of vitamins, minerals or healthy fats. Many of these products often boast that they are healthy and sugar free, but when you read the label, they use fructose or corn syrup and contain trans-fats. For these reasons, they are not recommended as part of this program.

CHEMICAL CUISINE

CHEMICAL: noun. 1. Noxious substances from which moderns foods are made.

Eating high quality foods are imperative today. When you purchase foods with chemical additives, you run the risk of harming your health. Instead, make a choice; go against the grain, change your pattern of eating. Choose wisely, read labels and purchase whole foods.

Chemical Additives & Their Health Effects

TABLE 2.2

NAME OF ADDITIVE	WHAT FOODS HAVE THESE ADDITIVES?	HEALTH EFFECTS
ACESULFAME-K	**Artificial Sweetener:** *Baked goods* *Chewing gum* *Gelatin desserts* *Diet soda*	Acesulfame K contains carcinogen methylene chloride. Long-term exposure to methylene chloride can cause headaches, depression, nausea, mental confusion, liver effects, kidney effects, visual disturbances, and cancer in humans.
ASPARTAME	***Artificial Sweetener:** *Candies* *Desserts* *Sugar free drinks* *Tabletop sweeteners*	Can cause problems with vision, as well as neurologic, psychological, psychiatric, gastrointestinal, endocrine, metabolic, skin and allergy issues.
BUTYLATED HYDROXYANISOLE (BHA)	**Antioxidant:** *Cereals* *Chewing gum* *Potato chips* *Oils*	Can contribute to tumors, health and behavior issues. Possibly carcinogenic to humans.
PROPYL GALLATE	**Antioxidant Preservative:** *Vegetable oil* *Meat products* *Potato sticks* *Chicken soup base* *Gum*	Can cause eczema, stomach problems and hyper-activity.
SODIUM NITRITE, SODIUM NITRATE	**Preservative, coloring, flavoring:** *Bacon* *Ham* *Frankfurters* *Lunch meats* *Smoked fish* *Corned beef*	Has been suspected of being a cause of stomach cancer.

*Also known as NutraSweet® and Equal®

GENETIC ENGINEERING OF FOODS (GMO, GM)

"According to a 1999 Acres USA article, cattle even broke through a fence and walked through a field of Roundup Ready corn (GMO) to get to a non-GM variety that they ate. The cows left the GM corn untouched."

Technically fraught with unknown consequences for our health and our planet, Genetically Modified Foods (GMO), or "Franken Foods" are the by-products of splicing genes from one species into the DNA of another. Genetic engineering is described as the manipulation of plant and animal development by altering the gene expression in a plant or animal.[28] These types of foods have been shown to negatively impact a person's health. Containing fewer nutrients than conventionally grown foods, studies have chronicled that rats that were fed these foods, had damaged immune systems.[29]

Additionally, genetic modification introduces allergens into foods. Genetic engineering affects livestock and milk products. Commercial cows' milk from hybrid cows is questionable because GMO milk often irritates our intestines and contributes to leaky gut syndrome. This alarming health issue occurs when large spaces develop between the cells of the gut wall allowing bacteria, toxins and food to leak into the bloodstream. Leaky Gut Syndrome symptoms vary and include: abdominal pain, heartburn, insomnia, bloating, anxiety, gluten intolerance, malnutrition, muscle cramps and pains, poor exercise tolerance and food allergies.

Leaky Gut Syndrome has also been linked to: Celiac disease, (gluten sensitivity) Multiple Sclerosis, Fibromylagia, Autism, Chronic Fatigue Syndrome, Irritable Bowel Syndrome, Eczema, Dermatitis, and Ulcerative Colitis.

The most common engineered/hybridized foods are wheat, beef, soy, and white corn. Newer GMO's to be aware of are salmon, alfalfa and beet sugar.

DOES ORGANIC MEAN THAT THE FOOD IS NON-GMO?

If a package states that it is 100 percent organic, each ingredient by law must comply with that standard. If the label says "Organic" at least 95 percent must be organic. According to the organic standards, the other 5 percent should not be GMO. If the label on a food states "made with organic ingredients, approximately 70 percent of the ingredients must be organic- and the remaining 30 percent should not be GM.[30] For a full list of foods that are GMO free and contain GMO ingredients by brand name, please visit http://www.seedsofdeception. com/documentFiles/144.pdf.

You can also visit http://www.nong-moshoppingguide.com/SG/TipsforA-voidingGMOs/index.cfm

Now that you have learned about the different food groups, how do you know which foods are specifically best for you? One of the best ways to address this concern is through nutritional balancing science. This is the solution many of us have been seeking.

Recommended Foods for the Nutritional Balancing Program

TABLE 2.3

		BEST FOODS	GOOD FOODS	OCCASIONAL	BEST AVOIDED
VEGETABLES	**ROOT**	• Beets (golden) • Carrots • Celery root • Garlic • Onions • Parsnips • Rutabagas • Sweet potatoes • Turnips • Yams • 10-12 oz. of carrot juice or 1-2 oz wheatgrass	• Red beets • Zucchini	• All peppers • Eggplant • Potatoes • Tomatoes * *Nightshade vegetables like these can increase inflammation and arthritic tendencies.*	
	CRUCIFEROUS	• Broccoli • Cabbage (red/green) • Brussels sprouts • Cauliflower			
	LEAFY	• Bok choy • Swiss chard • Kale • Spinach • Collard • Mustard • Beet greens		• Lettuce	
	SQUASH		• Summer squash	• Winter squashes (Acorn & butternut) • Spaghetti squash	
PROTEINS		• Free range, organic eggs • Lamb • Chicken or turkey • Wild game • Sardines • Almond butter or Almonds • Organic pistachio nuts (bragafarms.com)	• Beans • All other nuts and seed butters, • Salmon-one time a month • Standard eggs	• Beef • Peanut butter and peanuts • Soy products	• Bacon • Ham • Large fish • Pork • Processed cheese • Processed meats • Sausage • Shark • Swordfish • Tile fish • Tuna
SPICES		• Indian spices • Kelp • Hawaiian jade sea salt • Mustard	• Other mild spices	• Sea vegetables, other than kelp	• Table salt • All very hot spices

		BEST FOODS	GOOD FOODS	OCCASIONAL	BEST AVOIDED
CARBOHYDRATES	COMPLEX	• Brown rice • Buckwheat • Organic blue and yellow corn chips and tortillas • Quinoa • Green lentils	• Lentils & other dried beans • White rice • Basmati • Yellow corn • Barley • Rye • Oats	• Tofu & tempeh	• *All wheat products, including, white flours, whole wheat products, and organic whole wheat products.* • *Many people are also sensitive to spelt products as well.* • Red potatoes • Soy • White potatoes
CARBOHYDRATES	SIMPLE FRUIT & SWEETENERS	• Botija olives, dried		• Raw uncooked honey • 100 Percent natural maple syrup • Agave nectar • Fruit • Mannitol • Sorbitol • Xylitol • Stevia	• Cakes • Candy • Canned foods with sugar • Chocolate • Cookies • Protein bars • Ice cream • Sugared cereals • White flour • White sugar • All fruit juices • All preservatives, additives, chemicals and artificial sweeteners, fillers • Aspartame • Equal • NutraSweet • Saccharine • Splenda
FATS & OILS		• Butter • Egg yolk • Chicken, turkey, beef or lamb fat. • Sardines or occasional salmon • Toasted almond butter	• Olive oil • Other nut & seed butters	• Coconut oil • Canola • Corn oil • Peanut • Safflower • Sesame • Sunflower	• Hydrogenated oils • Margarine • Trans-fats • Commercial peanut butter • Lard
BEVERAGES		• Spring water • Mild herbal teas • Raw goat or cow milk (see below regarding dairy) • Distilled water- for three months only	• Treated water • Sparkling Spring water, • Black, green and white teas • Carbon filtered water	• Organic wine —once a week, but not highly recommended • Sanka or other grain beverages	• Alcohol • Artificially sweetened iced teas • Fruit juices • Low calorie drink mixes • Soda and soft drinks • Reverse osmosis • Alkaline water • Unfiltered tap water
DAIRY		• Organic or preferably raw certified cow or goat products, such as milk, plain yogurt, kefir and cheese		• Regular dairy products	• Chocolate milk • Processed cheese

CHAPTER
three

what is nutritional balancing science?

Nutritional balancing involves an integration of scientific systems concepts both ancient and modern and is a formula for anyone who wants improved health. It focuses on the underlying stress response patterns in the human body, rather than chasing symptoms.

A healing system that draws from many branches of science, nutritional balancing incorporates knowledge from the fields of biochemistry, physiology, nutrition, stress theory, pathology, psychology, and ancient ones as well, like acupuncture. It also offers specific applications of hair tissue mineral analysis, diet, supplementary nutrients, detoxification protocols, and lifestyle changes to raise one's energy level as a means to restore balance.

Healing is a matter of time, but it is sometimes also a matter of opportunity.

Hippocrates

DYNAMIC EQUILIBRIUM

This science is designed to restore healthier homeostatic states.[31] Homeostasis is the process of maintaining internal system equilibrium or balance in the face of constantly changing conditions. In the body, the changing conditions might include your temperature, your energy level or even your mood. The body must keep itself balanced, heated properly, and be able to digest food in the face of a constantly shifting internal and external environment. The goal of nutritional balancing is to move the body from a less desirable homeostatic state to a more desirable one. By restoring homeostasis and energy production, nutritional balancing can improve your health and your vitality.

NUTRITIONAL BALANCING VS. TRADITIONAL MODEL OF MEDICINE

This paradigm differs from the conceptual model of traditional medicine because standard medical treatment names a disease or a condition and then prescribes a remedy or treatment. For example, if you have an ulcer, you are given medicine as a remedy to the health condition. In contrast, nutritional balancing usually does not need to name the condition, but rather seeks to understand the biochemical imbalances that are causing it. By correcting the biochemistry, healing generally occurs easily.

HOW DID NUTRITIONAL BALANCING DEVELOP?

Dr. Paul Eck, the founder of nutritional balancing was responsible for the research done in the area of nutritional balancing science. He read both textbooks of western and Oriental healing systems and realized that increasing a person's vitality was a key to healing. Nutrition was the most basic and powerful way to balance body chemistry. Dr. Eck primarily based his research on two of his most important mentors. They were George Watson, PhD, and Hans Selye, M.D.

DR. WATSON AND THE OXIDATION TYPES

George Watson, PhD, a researcher at the University of California-Los Angeles discovered and later coined the term fast and slow oxidizers, now a key term used in nutritional balancing. He believed that fast oxidizers, burned fats more efficiently, while the other group, slow oxidizers, burned carbohydrates more efficiently. He used the word oxidation because it referred to the burning of calories in the body.

However, his most important work was his brilliant manner of correcting the oxidation rate. He employed dietary modifications and simple supplements to bring balance to the body. He ascertained that a high fat diet slowed the oxidation rate, whereas, a diet higher in protein and carbohydrates and lower in fats and oils enhanced or sped up the oxidation rate.

Moreover, he found that nutritional supplements including calcium, magnesium, copper and vitamins A and D in certain dosages tended to slow the oxidation rate. On the other hand, he found that supplements such as vitamins B complex, C and E, zinc and manganese increased the oxidation rate.

Additionally, Dr. Watson observed that when the oxidation rate became balanced, a person's energy level improved drastically, showed significant improvement and an array of both physical and emotional symptoms disappeared. Yet, if a person stayed on one formula and one diet too long, the oxidation rate would over correct and symptoms would reappear. He learned that he needed to shift the diet and supplements to adjust the oxidation rate back to its ideal state. This concept was later adopted by Dr. Eck and used as part of this regimen.

DR. SELYE & THE STRESS THEORY OF DISEASE

Dr. Hans Selye, M.D. was a brilliant and accomplished researcher who was credited with the stress theory of disease. He learned that the body reacts to stress in specific states, which he called the general adaption syndrome and stages of stress.[32,33]

These three stages of biochemical stress include—alarm, resistance, and exhaustion. The alarm stage is considered an early stage of stress in which the body fights back against stress. The resistance stage occurs when the body can no longer maintain an alarm stage, but can resist stress. Lastly, is the exhaustion stage of stress, which occurs when the body has exhausted its energy reserves and can no longer resist stress very well. This discovery has placed his research into mainstream physiology books.

Dr. Eck incorporated Dr. Seyle's research in the nutritional balancing program. Additionally, foods, vitamins and minerals, rest and sleep, lifestyle changes and detoxification protocols are used to help restore the body's ability to respond to stress. (See Appendix A and B for additional information.) These modalities can help shift the body to adapt in ways that will promote health, using nutrition as a method to adjust the body in a direction—of equilibrium and thus, healing.[34] After years of research, Dr. Eck then synthesized all of these scientific concepts, along with his own extensive and far reaching research, to provide an extraordinary framework for nutritional balancing science.

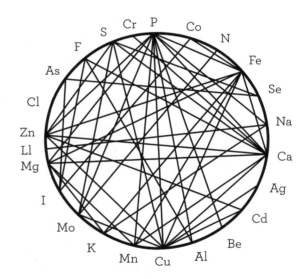

MINERAL WHEEL

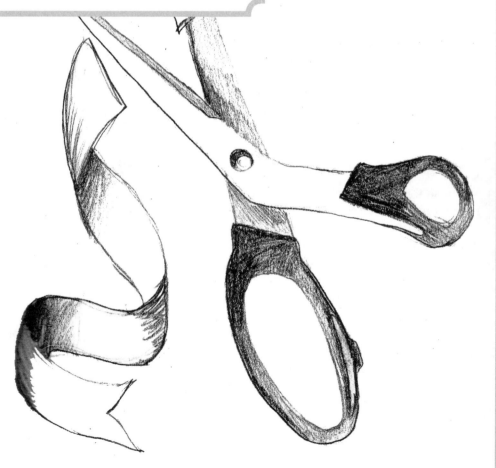

CHAPTER
four

 *getting started*

ON THE NUTRITIONAL BALANCING PROGRAM

Everyone is entitled to optimal health. Being healthy means feeling energized as well as emotionally balanced. Being healthy means far more than just waking up and getting out of bed each day. When your body is healthy, you exude vivacity, a sense of well-being.

The information, menus and recipes provided herein lay the groundwork for good health through proper diet. When illness strikes, it is even more critical that you fortify your body with the nutrients that are necessary to heal.

The foods and general supplements recommended in this volume are essential to build strong new cells and boost the immune system. The right foods help the body to heal, just as the wrong foods can trigger illness and avoidable signs of aging.

Let's begin this exciting new venture by educating and explaining the basic concepts that underlie this program.

A Journey of a thousand miles must begin with a single step.

Lao-tzu, The Way of Lao-Tzu

DIETARY CONCEPTS FOR EVERYONE

WHAT TO EAT

The nutritional balancing dietary regimen is comprised of the following foods:

① **A variety of steamed organic vegetables filling one half to two thirds of your plate.**

The emphasis is on vegetables and on cooking them. This is very important. Vegetables provide hundreds of extremely usable nutrients, are highly nutritious, somewhat more yang in nature, (more warming) and are very alkaline in their reaction in the body.

STEAMING VEGETABLES:

- *Helps break down indigestible fibers, allowing much better absorption of most nutrients, particularly minerals,*

- *Concentrates many foods, such as spinach, allowing you to eat more vegetables at a meal,*

- *Adds heat or yang energy,*

- *Kills literally thousands of surface bacteria, fungi, parasites and other harmful organisms. Most people do not have enough stomach acid to kill microorganisms on some food. Also much of our food is grown out of the country where standards of cleanliness are often much lower, increasing the chances for food-borne infections.*

② **Natural and organic grass fed meats that include poultry, lamb, and eggs.**

We are indeed much more than what we eat, but what we eat can nevertheless help us to be much more than what we are.

Adele Davis—pioneer in the field of nutrition during the mid-20th century. Author of Let's Have Healthy Children, Let's Eat Right to Keep Fit, and Let's Get Well.

③ **Fish**

Fish is a special case. It is a nutritious food, but filled with mercury today. Very small fish however are highly recommended. Sardines, herrings, anchovies, smelt, and salmon—once a month only, because it is a larger fish and may contain more mercury than smaller fish.

④ **Small amounts blue and yellow organic corn products, and wheat-free grains such as brown rice, millet and quinoa.**

⑤ **Some high quality organic, full fat dairy, as raw as possible (Certified)**[35]

Certified raw dairy products from grass-fed cows (fed pasture, hay and silage), produced under clean conditions and promptly refrigerated, contains many anti-microbial and immune-supporting components that can energize the body. This includes milk, cheese and yogurt.

⑥ **Some healthful animal fats and oils such as butter, egg yolks, and a small amount of vegetable oils, olive oil, flax oil and hemp seed oil.**
Cooking fats and oils can damage these foods' nutritional qualities, some more than others. Therefore, try eating all meats lightly cooked and all eggs soft boiled, poached or lightly scrambled because it helps to maintain the food's optimal nutritional status. If you use vegetable oils, buy only cold pressed, raw, organic oils. Raw flaxseed or hempseed oils are excellent products because they are rich in Omega-3's, but watch the expiration dates since they go rancid quickly.

⑦ **Minimal amount of fruit**
Fruit is very yin, quite hybridized, and its sweetness tends to upset the blood sugar level in most people causing a variety of symptoms such as anxiety, fatigue or headaches. If you need to have fruit, limit it to berries or an apple once a day.

⑧ **Ten to twelve ounces of fresh or store bought carrot juice**
Freshly juiced carrots, provides a highly bioavailable form of calcium and other nutrients. Fresh or frozen wheatgrass is also an excellent alternative as well, and it is recommended that you have one or two ounces of this juice. If you would like, try adding a few vegetables to your carrot juice.

PURE AND SIMPLE
Keep meals honest, clean and simple for best digestion. Many people believe meals should be complex. In fact, a meal with a protein and two types of vegetables are plenty as it eases digestion. Straightforward and organic food is best to maintain balanced in the body.

MIX IT UP
Try not to eat the same food two or three days in a row, if possible, so that you get a variety of assorted nutrients in your diet.

WHAT NOT TO EAT
You should buy only whole foods, those in which nothing has been added and those in which nothing has been removed; cooking for good health means using ingredients that have not been processed or stripped of their vital nutrients. Omit the following foods and read the labels as you shop:

- **All sugars and sweets**
- **Wheat in all forms, and most spelt**
- **Artificial sweeteners**
- **Alcohol**
- **Most caffeine**
- **Juices and Smoothies, except 10-12 ounces of carrot juice, and 1-2 ounces of wheatgrass juice**
- **Preservatives**
- **Most nuts and seeds—too yin**
- **Chemical additives**
- **Pesticide sprayed foods**
- **Toxic metals (most fish, all shellfish and seafood)**
- **Unhealthy fats**
- **Processed foods**
- **Fast foods**

RECOMMENDED SUPPLEMENTS — HELPFUL FOR ALMOST EVERYONE
(ADULTS ONLY)

The supplements listed below are not a complete list, but are those recommendations that nutritional balancing suggests.

OMEGA-3 FATTY ACIDS SUCH AS FISH OIL
(1000 MG. DAILY)

This fatty acid is necessary because it performs a number of important functions in the body:

- *Keeps cell membranes flexible. This allows for the transfer of nutrients and waste products in and out of the cell.*

- *Helps to keep the skin and mucus membranes moist.*

- *Produce hormones that can help maintain heart rate, blood clotting and inflammation.*

- *Obtain needed nutrition and dispose of harmful waste products.*

- *Necessary for nerve transmission.*

- *Aids in fighting infections.*

- *Assists in proper growth in children.*

- *Lack or imbalance of this fat is linked to Heart Attacks, Cancer, Depression, Lupus, Asthma, Obesity, ADHD and Alzheimer's.*

- *Prevents inflammation.*

However if you do not want to take Omega-3 in a supplement form, please eat three cans of sardines per week and follow the general dietary guidelines provided herein.

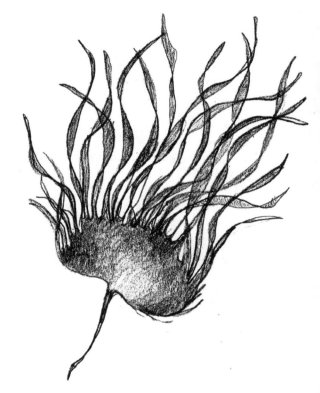

KELP
(600 MG - ONE CAPSULE THREE TIMES A DAY)

Kelp grows along rocky shores and is recommended because:

- *It is an excellent source of approximately 20-30 trace minerals.*

- *It is an outstanding source of iodine, an important mineral needed for thyroid hormone production, and other trace minerals.*

- *It contains chemicals called alginates, which bind and remove the mercury it contains.*

- *Exceptions: avoid kelp if you have Grave's disease or hyperthyroidism.*

VITAMIN D3
5000 IU'S DAILY

This vitamin can be taken in the form of cod liver oil or simply as a vitamin D3 capsule. This vitamin is important to the body because it plays a major role in maintaining the proper amounts of calcium and phosphorus necessary to keep bones strong. Vitamin D is necessary because it helps to:

* *Prevent Osteoporosis.*

* *Prevent Rickets.*

* *Reduce the risk of Diabetes.*

* *Reduce the risk of certain Cancers, especially Colon, Prostate, and Breast cancer.*

* *Prevent Bone Fractures.*

* *Reduce risk of Multiple Sclerosis.*

* *Reduce Anxiety.*

> The doctor of the future will give no medication, but will interest his patients in the care of the human frame, diet and in the cause and prevention of disease.
>
> *Thomas A Edison*

CALCIUM / MAGNESIUM
750MG OF CALCIUM AND 450MG OF MAGNESIUM TAKEN DAILY ONE –TWO CAPSULES DAILY

Calcium is the most plentiful element in the body, with most in the bones, teeth and nerves. Calcium helps regulate cell permeability, is critical for maintenance of acid-base balance, and assists in hormone secretion, cell division and osmotic balance. It stabilizes cell membranes, helps relax muscles and slows nerve transmission and heart rate.

Magnesium is needed for calcium absorption and also aids in muscle relaxation. It also acts as a coenzyme that constructs proteins, which build your body, and prevents constipation.

WHAT ARE THE BEST WAYS TO OBTAIN VITAMIN D?

1. Sunshine

2. Full-spectrum light- GE Reveal® 100 Watt bulb shining on your bare chest for approximately 15-30 minutes daily.

3. Supplements

4. Cod liver oil

ZINC
10-20MG PER DAY
ONE CAPSULE THREE TIMES DAILY

This mineral is important to your health because it is required for hundreds of enzymatic reactions in the body that play a role in eyesight, hearing, skin, hair, nails, connective tissue, sexual function, digestion and many more functions.

VITAMIN C
500 MG PER DAY

Required for the growth and repair of tissues in all parts of your body. Needed to form collagen, an important protein used to make skin, scar tissue, tendons, ligaments, and blood vessels. Vitamin C is essential for the healing of wounds, and for the repair and maintenance of cartilage, bones, and teeth.

Excellent nutrition and recommended supplementation will help you stay healthy. It will also help you heal. The information provided by hair tissue mineral analysis, one aspect of nutritional balancing science, offers a wonderful way to jump start your program.

HAIR TISSUE MINERAL ANALYSIS: A USEFUL TOOL

The more knowledge you have about your body, the more you can help yourself reclaim and maintain good health. Hair tissue mineral analysis, one aspect of the nutritional balancing program is an excellent way to find out what your body needs. This screening tool accurately tests for carbohydrate tolerance and energy levels. It can expose the causes of poor heath and pinpoint tendencies for dozens of illnesses even before the onset of obvious symptoms.

A soft tissue mineral biopsy detects vitamin deficiencies as well as mineral levels. It also detects toxic metals. (See Appendix C) While it is not intended to diagnose disease, it's a revealing method, exposing the harmful (as well as helpful) minerals and metals in the body. By eliminating toxic metals, balancing minerals and enhancing your diet with essential vitamins and nutrients, you can restore the body to a healthier state.

OXIDATION TYPES AND THEIR RECOMMENDED DIETS

Our bodies are energy-producing machines. Every aspect of our well-being depends on adequate energy production. If we put the wrong fuel in our cars, they do not drive well. If we put the wrong food in our bodies, they can make us sick and tired. Hair tissue mineral analysis provides an assessment of an individual's oxidation rate, the rate at which the body burns or oxidizes food (energy). Discerning the oxidation rate is an important aspect of Metabolic Typing for it allows individuals to adjust their diets to address their own personal needs.

Dr. George Watson, author of *Nutrition and your Mind*, Bantam Books, 1972, based the concept of Metabolic Typing on results he saw as he researched aspects of human metabolism. However, it was Dr. Paul Eck, who was the first person to identify and correlate hair mineral ratios with oxidation types. As mentioned previously, there are two main types of oxidation rates: slow and fast. The slow oxidizer is an individual who metabolizes food at a rate slower than required for the production of energy while the fast oxidizer is an individual who metabolizes food at a rate faster than required for the production of energy.

Try thinking of the oxidation rate as being comparable to a car's engine that runs at the proper speed. In the body, various systems run at optimal rates, such as nutrient levels, and temperature. When the system is balanced, it produces far more energy with less chance of breakdown. For instance, in slow oxidation, the body's engine runs cold, analogous to a cold car engine, which does not produce optimal power. Similarly, if the body's engine runs too hot, eventually, it will damage the body. When the speed or oxidation rate is equalized, not too fast or too slow, performance is enhanced.

Excellent nutrition will help you stay healthy as well as help you heal. When you choose the correct foods, you optimize vital energy capable of being produced by the body. The information provided by hair tissue mineral analysis[36] offers a wonderful way to jump start your program. Eating a diet suitable for one's oxidation type is a primary healing modality.

> The hair mineral test gives a unique type of reading. It measures activity within the tissues without requiring expensive biopsies or other procedures. Since most metabolic activity occurs within the tissues rather than the blood, the hair test provides a different point of view.
>
> *Dr. Lawrence Wilson, M.D.*

DIET FOR THE SLOW OXIDIZER

(See Page 74 for a five day menu)

The diet for those with slow oxidation consists of cooked vegetables, ten to twelve ounces of freshly juiced carrots, adequate protein and healthy fats, some complex carbohydrates and minimal amounts of fruits. These foods not only help support adrenal and thyroid activity, but also stabilize blood sugar. Vegetables are emphasized because they are nutrient rich, yang in nature, and very alkaline in their reaction in the body. They also provide hundreds of nutrients in an extremely usable form. Steamed vegetables, are recommended at least twice a day, and should cover at least one half to two thirds (you can also think of this as a double or triple serving size) of your plate at lunch and dinner. Root vegetables such as turnips, parsnips, carrots, rutabaga, daikon and celery root are excellent choices because they are rich in minerals. Dark green leafy vegetables are also wonderful choices because of their high magnesium content.

This diet helps maintain and increase energy. A slow oxidizer's protein intake is set at approximately 20 percent of his or her dietary intake or approximately 10-15 ounces daily.

The proteins recommended include:

- **Chicken**
- **Turkey and lean meats**
- **Fish**
- **Eggs**
- **Plain yogurt**
- **Beans**

Those with slow oxidation do well on this diet because they are given foods to optimize their energy. As their oxidation rate slows further, they often become apathetic and depressed. Their blood pressure and blood sugar may be low unless arteriosclerosis or diabetes has set in. Their skin and hair are often dry, and their hair may become brittle or thin. Many experience constipation and other symptoms associated with reduced adrenal and thyroid glandular activity. Those with slow oxidation may gain weight on the hips and the legs due to their metabolic imbalance.

OXIDATION

Slow and fast oxidation can be compared to the story of *The Tortoise and the Hare*. The slow oxidizer is similar to the tortoise in that he is sluggish and slow-moving, but nonetheless, always steady. The fast oxidizer is similar to the hare in that he is swift and quick, but can tire quickly, necessitating a nap.

DIET FOR THE FAST OXIDIZER

(See Page 76 for a five day menu)

The diet for those with fast oxidation consists of fewer carbohydrates, more fats and oils, proteins, occasionally—minimal fruit such as an apple or berries. Fats and oils are absorbed and utilized more slowly than sugars and tend to decelerate the oxidation process keeping serum glucose levels more consistent. Sugars, as well as carbohydrates which convert to sugar, are absorbed and burned more quickly than fats. This affects blood sugar levels, which fluctuate more in a fast oxidizer if they do not follow this recommended diet. These rapid oscillations can lead to hypoglycemic episodes, binge eating, cravings, weight gain, hyperkinesis, panic attacks, diabetes, and other disorders.

Proteins that are higher in fat are recommended for the fast oxidizer because they help keep the blood sugar more stable. Steamed vegetables should cover half to two thirds of your plate (you can also think of this as a double or triple serving size). The information provided previously regarding the importance of vegetables applies here as well.

The proteins recommended for the fast oxidizer include approximately 8-13 ounces of protein daily or more if necessary as well as the following foods:

- Lamb
- Dark meat chicken and turkey
- Sardines, caviar, anchovies, herring, and salmon-one time a month, only occasional consumption of beef is recommended.
- At least two tablespoons of a high quality fat or oil for adults with every meal as listed in Table 2.3. More is acceptable if desired, as long as you do not overeat. Children, who are fast oxidizers should have Omega-3's , although these are important for everyone today.

A NOTE ON GRAINS AND STARCHES:

- Reduce or eliminate most heavy starches such as grains. Try to limit starchy vegetables such as sweet potatoes, yams, and parsnips as well because grains and starches are higher in carbohydrates and are broken down and used by the body quickly.
- Fast oxidizers will often crave starches and sweets if they do not eat enough fats and oil with each meal.

HIGH QUALITY FATS AND OILS:

- Digest and release energy slowly
- Provide acetates. These are high-energy compounds found only in fats and a few other products found which fast oxidizers need.

FIVE DAYS OF MENUS

The meal plans for the slow and fast oxidizers are recommended meals only. Please feel free to adjust the menus (within the guidelines, of course) according to your dietary tastes.

This program does not recommend specific quantities of foods, as people's needs vary due to their age, height, weight, activity level, occupation and various other factors.

These menus were crafted to help you understand how to create balanced meals so that you can achieve vitality and health. Please do not feel restricted to follow these menus exactly, as they are just a way for you to follow along until you feel comfortable creating your own healthy meals.

① **Rotate your ingredients.**
Do not eat the same meat or vegetable several nights in a row.

② **Please eat snacks only if needed.**
They are included because some people need them. (If you are hypoglycemic or very tempted to eat the wrong foods, it is recommended that you eat small meals every few hours.)

③ **Don't drink with meals.**
Drinking water with meals dilutes stomach acid and digestive juices. Drink water and tea an hour after meals and up to 10 minutes before the meal or in between meals to best support digestion.

④ **Leftovers are good for a day or two.**
Food may become rancid if left in the refrigerator for longer periods of time.

Look through the recipe section of the book and create your own wonderful, simple meals.

If you would like more specific guidelines regarding nutritional balancing, it is recommended that you work with a practitioner, as the program is powerful. Please see www.drlwilson.com for a list of recommended practitioner's in your area.

When diet is wrong
medicine is of no use.
When diet is correct
medicine is of no need.

Ayurvedic Proverb

Slow Oxidizer Diet

Please make sure to have protein at least twice a day, as well as a
small serving of complex carbohydrates twice a day and loads of vegetables.

MONDAY

Upon Arising	1 quart spring water—hot water is best, room temperature is acceptable. (Drinking water upon awakening is an excellent habit to develop as it is one method to help you drink the recommended amount of water daily.)
	10-12 ounces of carrot juice—before breakfast
Breakfast	Two poached eggs with steamed spinach, a serving of blue corn chips
Snack	Cooked green beans with some yogurt and dill dip
Lunch	Chicken Stir-Fry with ½ cup of brown rice. *(See page 143 for recipe)*
Snack	Hummus and carrots
Dinner	Leftovers
Beverage	1 pot (1 quart) of chamomile herbal tea

TUESDAY

Upon Arising	1 quart spring water—hot water is best, room temperature is acceptable.
	10-12 ounces of carrot juice—before breakfast
Breakfast	A Different Kind of Delightful Pancake. *(See page 202 for recipe)*
Snack	¼ of head cooked cauliflower, with some yogurt dip
Lunch	Roasted chicken, double or triple serving of cooked broccoli and/or brown rice tortilla or corn tortilla
Snack	A few rice crackers with tahini or yogurt dip
Dinner	Spinach Lentil Soup *(See page 164 for recipe)*
Beverage	1 pot (1 quart) of apple spice herbal tea

WEDNESDAY

Upon Arising	1 quart spring water—hot water is best, room temperature is acceptable. 10-12 ounces of carrot juice- before breakfast
Breakfast	Mexican Scrambled Eggs *(includes a handful of blue corn chips. See page 129 for recipe)*
Snack	Cooked carrots with tahini
Lunch	Easy Roll Ups—Smoked Salmon and Goat Cheese *(See page 149 for recipe)* double or triple serving steamed broccoli
Snack	Leftovers from yesterday's lunch
Dinner	Hot cereal (brown rice cereal) and double or triple serving of frozen peas
Beverages	Make a pot (1 quart) of peach tea between meals.

THURSDAY

Upon Arising	1 quart spring—hot water is best, room temperature is acceptable. 10-12 ounces of carrot juice—before breakfast
Breakfast	Brown Rice Belly Warmer *(See Page 135 for recipe)*
Snack	Almond butter on a few rice crackers
Lunch	From Down Under the Sea Nori Roll-Up *(See Page 149 for recipe)* double or triple serving steamed of sautéed beet greens
Snack	Cooked Brussels sprouts and yogurt dip
Dinner	Sardines in the Pan with Garlic *(See page 151 for recipe)*, double or triple serving steamed cabbage and a small sweet potato
Beverages	Make a pot (1 quart) of hibiscus tea between meals.

FRIDAY

Upon Arising	1 quart spring water—hot water is best, room temperature is acceptable. 10-12 ounces of carrot juice—before breakfast
Breakfast	2-3 eggs softly cooked on a bed of steamed kale, toasted brown rice tortilla
Snack	Sunflower seed butter on celery
Lunch	Quick and Easy Onion Soup *(See page 163 for recipe)*, double or triple serving Jazzy Green Beans and Garlic *(See page 174 for recipe)*, ½ cup of Brown Rice Parmesan *(See page 184 for recipe)*
Dinner	Grilled chicken, double or triple serving steamed broccoli, and ½ cup of quinoa
Beverages	Make a pot (1 quart) of mint tea between meals.

Fast Oxidizer Diet

Please remember to have 1-2 tablespoons of healthful fats or oils with each meal and minimize your complex carbohydrates, fruits and other sweets.

MONDAY

Upon Arising	1 quart spring hot water is best, room temperature is acceptable. (Drinking water upon awakening is an excellent habit to develop as it is one method to help you drink the recommended amount of water daily.)
	10-12 ounces of carrot juice—before breakfast
Breakfast	2-3 eggs omelet softly cooked (mushy, if possible) with broccoli and just a few blue corn chips
Snack	Toasted almond butter with a few rye crackers
Lunch	Large bowl of thick Cream of Broccoli Soup *(See page 159 for recipe)*
Snack	½ cup of whole milk cottage cheese, or other full fat cheese
Dinner	1 can of sardines packed in oil, double or triple serving of steamed Swiss chard and cabbage topped with butter
Beverages	Make a pot (1 quart) of orange tea between meals.

TUESDAY

Upon Arising	1 quart spring water-hot water is best, room temperature is acceptable.
	10-12 ounces of carrot juice—before breakfast
Breakfast	2-3 Simply Soft Boiled Eggs *(See page 134 for recipe)* with ½ cup of cooked oatmeal
Snack	1 cup of full fat plain yogurt
Lunch	Turkey drumstick, double or triple serving of Golden Beets Galore *(See page 179 for recipe)*
Snack	Steamed broccoli with butter or with a chunk of cheese
Dinner	Megan's Twist on Macaroni and Cheese *(See page 214 for recipe)*
Beverages	Make a pot (1 quart) of strawberry tea between meals.

WEDNESDAY

Upon Arising	1 quart spring water—hot water is best, room temperature is acceptable.
	10-12 ounces of carrot juice—before breakfast
Breakfast	Leftovers from yesterday's lunch or dinner.
Snack	Cashew butter on a couple of blue corn chips
Lunch	Grilled and Glazed Lamb Burgers *(See page 152 for recipe)*, double or triple serving of steamed Brussels sprouts
Snack	Sunflower butter on rice crackers
Dinner	Grilled chicken and ½ plate or more of Steamin' Demon Veggies *(See page 217 for recipe)*
Beverages	Make a pot (1 quart) of hibiscus tea between meals.

THURSDAY

Upon Arising	1 quart spring water—hot water is best, room temperature is acceptable.
	10-12 ounces of carrot juice—before breakfast
Breakfast	Eggy Veggie Stir Fry *(See page 131 for recipe)*
Snack	Cooked carrots with butter or coconut oil
Lunch	Small steak up to 5-6 ounce, double or triple serving of Olive Oils' Specialty *(See page 176 for recipe)* ½ cup of brown rice
Snack	Small serving of blue corn chips
Dinner	Chicken and Cauliflower (double or triple serving size) with Infused Indian Flavors *(See page 142 for recipe)*
Beverages	Make a pot (1 quart) of hibiscus tea between meals.

FRIDAY

Upon Arising	1 quart spring water—hot water is best, room temperature is acceptable.
	10-12 ounces of carrot juice—before breakfast
Breakfast	Double portion of turnips with butter and ½ cup of leftover lentils.
Snack	Toasted almond butter on rye crackers
Lunch	Chicken Stir Fry *(See page 143 for recipe)* and ½ cup of brown rice
Snack	Leftovers from last nights dinner or ½ cup of whole milk cottage cheese
Dinner	Poached Eggs in a Green Nest *(See page 132 for recipe)*, corn tortilla with butter and double or triple serving of cooked carrots.
Beverages	Make a pot (1 quart) of raspberry tea between meals.

This food is the gift of the whole universe—
The Earth, the sky, and much hard work.

May we eat in mindfulness so as to
be worthy to receive it.

May we transform our unskillful states of mind
And learn to eat with moderation.

May we take only foods that nourish us
and prevent illness.

We accept this food to realize the path of
understanding and love.

Thich Nhat Hanh, (Plum Village Chanting and recitation Book, 2000.)

EATING HABITS

Commonly overlooked, but an important aspect of being healthy, is having good eating habits. Below is a list of recommendations to ensure optimal health:

① **Rest 5-10 minutes** *if possible, before you begin eating your meal.*

② **Have relaxed sit down meals.**

③ **Chew your food thoroughly,** *at least ten times or even more.*

④ **Rotate your diet** *and try to avoid eating the same food no more than every third day, if possible. This helps with any food sensitivities and also has the added bonus of increasing the variety of nutrients that you consume.*

⑤ **Avoid eating in the car or noisy places** *as it can interfere with proper digestion.*

MINDFUL BITES

Most of us don't think about what we are eating; rather all we are thinking about is the next bite. Many of us have not even tasted what we are swallowing. Here is suggestion. Try engaging in mindful eating. This is an excellent way to discover a far more satisfying relationship to food and eating. How do you do this? First, I would suggest that time is taken to appreciate the food on your plate, where it has come from, its colors, smells and textures. Then, once you bite into your food, chew slowly, tasting the delicious, mouthwatering fare you are eating. Savor your ability to sense flavor. This might sound simple, but it takes some discipline. With this small exercise you can begin to fully realize the what, how and why of what you are eating. Often, a different kind of nourishment emerges, the kind that offers satisfaction on a very deep emotional level.

MINDFUL EATING INVOLVES MANY COMPONENTS. IT CAN HELP WITH:

- Learning to make choices in the beginning or ending of a meal based on hunger and satiety cues;
- Learn to notice triggers for mindless eating. This might include your emotions, social pressures or even certain foods;
- Focusing on quality over quantity of what your eating;
- Appreciating the food and its experience.

---

⑥ **Do not eat when standing up** *or when upset or anxious as this too will interfere with digestion.*

⑦ **Do not drink a lot of liquids with meals** *as it can dilute the digestive juices and affect your digestion.*

⑧ **Eat small meals every few hours** *if you are hypoglycemic or very tempted to eat the wrong foods. Each small meal should include protein/vegetable/complex carbohydrate or starchy vegetable, and healthy fat. This helps stabilize blood sugar and offset hypo-glycemic tendencies. For example, a mid–afternoon snack might be a hard boiled egg and some cooked carrots with hummus, almond butter on a rice cracker or a piece of quality cheese. (See page 194 for some healthful snack ideas)*

In this food I see clearly the presence of the entire universe supporting my existence.

Thich Nhat Hanh, (Plum Village Chanting and recitation Book, 2000.)

CHANGING EATING HABITS

Many of you might be concerned about how to implement all of these recommended changes. Don't panic! You do not have to overhaul your diet all at once. Try making changes slowly, introducing a new food each week and removing an unhealthy food each week. Over time, these minor changes will reprogram the way you think of foods, all without the pressure of a quick change. Never undervalue the positives that you are crafting with small changes. Always remember that you are moving in the right direction to your goal of a million miles. Here are some suggestions:

- **Start with small steps.** *You do not need to make all of these changes in one day.*

- **Begin to let go of your emotional connection to sweets.** *Sugary food choices are often based on positive childhood memories.*

- **Practice Loving-Kindness to yourself daily** as recommended in the Introductory chapter of this book. *It will help you to develop a friendliness and gentleness to yourself as you progress on this new path.*

- **Remember that you are human;** *there will be occasional lapses. Do not be hard on yourself. Forgive yourself and just return to the program.*

- **The longer you stay away from poor quality food, the easier it will be for you to see how junk food really makes you feel.** *That in and of itself is a great motivator to keep you on this program.*

- **Get plenty of rest.** *Sleep deprivation and fatigue cause sugar and starch cravings.*

- **Reward yourself.** *For example, treat yourself to a long walk in the woods or on the beach, or even a massage. This does not include a sugary, candy treat.*

- **Join a support group** *or ask your family and friends to help you.*

- **Do not skip meals.** *Fatigue and hunger often lead to poor food choices.*

- **Drink a lot of clean water,** *preferably spring or distilled. Water helps you feel energized, aids circulation, lubricates the joints, helps the skin stay healthy as well as remove toxins from your body.*

- **Ignore misleading advertisements** *that boast quick energy fixes and Magic Bullet's™ for health. Poor quality and processed foods do not become nourishing because of fancy packaging and savvy advertising. Instead, these altered products will have you suffering health consequences.*

- **Minimize your time in front of the TV.** *This will reduce the amount of commercials that constantly bombard you with poor food choices and prescription drug fixes. Let's face it, how often do you see an advertisement for healthy vegetables on television.*

- **Wait a few minutes before giving into food cravings.** *Do some deep breathing or take your pet for a walk.*

- **Nourish, honor and respect yourself.** *You only have one body!*

- **Make your meals enjoyable.** *Do not watch TV, read the paper or a book while eating. Instead, enjoy the pleasurable new flavors of your food.*

- **Use butter as a topping,** *when beginning to add more vegetables into your dietary regime. Some other suggestions are to try almond butter (thinned down by adding a small amount of water), yogurt dressing, pesto sauce or even some tomato sauce.*

CHASING AWAY THAT SWEET TOOTH

A common concern I often hear is how do I satisfy my sweet tooth. Here are some suggestions:

- **Eat a diet that consists of many vegetables** *that are chewed well to obtain the most sweetness from food, and bringing out the natural flavors and sweetness. Complex carbohydrates, such as grains, legumes and vegetables become sweeter the longer they are chewed. If you continue this delicious habit, of consciously chewing your food, your cravings for sweets will gradually diminish and you will learn that simple balanced foods provide this satisfaction.*

- **Try eating sweet vegetables.** *This might include, beets, carrots, winter squash, sweet potatoes, and parsnips for dessert or in desserts.*

- **Eat something sour, pungent or spicy.** *It will help to minimize your cravings.*

- **Feel free to substitute stevia for sugar** *in your tea, coffee or yogurt.*

- **Gradually reducing your intake of sugars,** *using self-discipline, and self-reflection will help to move your through the withdrawal symptoms of tiredness, anxiety and depression.*

EATING OUT

I do not recommend eating out often. However, if you do, ask for exactly what you want if it is not on the menu. You may also want to ask for more vegetables, if they do not serve a large enough portion. If bread is served, ask the server to remove it from the table.

Ethnic foods such as East Indian, Chinese or Thai are the best options in many cases as they often make their food fresh. Please make sure that you inquire as to whether MSG is used, and if so simply ask them to not include it in your meal. Most restaurants are happy to accommodate your needs.

STRETCHING YOUR WALLET WITH NUTRITIONAL MEALS

Some experts say that it is virtually impossible to eat healthy on a tight budget. I disagree. Today, there are many options for those who need to watch their pocket-books and would like to improve their health. Below, I have provided you with various options that provide you with quality food, while watching your wallet, so that you can reclaim your health.

- **Buy in Bulk** *from discount warehouses. These stores make it affordable to eat well with tight purse strings. You can purchase large bags of rice and beans for far less than you would spend on fat laden preservative rich processed foods. You can also buy bulk packages of frozen vegetables, eggs, meats, and blocks of cheese.*

- **Run some frozen fruits through a juicer or a blender** *if you find yourself craving sweet foods, and add in some fresh cream/ whole milk. You can freeze this in ice cube trays with a popsicle stick and give it to the kids as a dessert. Another option is to make iced sherbet with this combination for dessert.*

- **Eat soups, stews, casseroles, crock-pot meals and chili recipes** *to stretch your dollar further.*

- **Buy a bag of onions**. *They are cheaper when purchased by the bag.*

- **Shop the perimeter (outside aisles)** *of the market so you fill your cart with healthy foods. Junk foods are fillers and they are pricey. An individual can of soda can cost anywhere from $.80 to $2.00 per can. Plus it is filled with up to 70 chemicals that are not even listed on the label. Sodas are usually made with tap water that is laden with toxic metals. These drinks are filled with anti-nutrients and chemicals. Remember, you can purchase a gallon of water for $.79 -$1.25 depending on where you shop. Save your money and your health and drink distilled or spring water. You can even purchase your water at local springs. (www.findaspring.com provides you with information on how to find a local spring near you where you can fill up your own water, often for free. Just bring your own bottles.)*

- **Purchase produce that is in season; it is cheaper.** *Eggs, chicken, sardines, and corn tortillas are some examples of inexpensive foods.*

- **Cook at home more often**. *Eating out is expensive and often not as healthy.*

- **Start a garden at home** *and grow your own vegetables.*

- **Do your best to avoid purchasing prepared foods.** *These foods are more money and have added chemicals and preservatives that are detrimental to your health.*

- **Forego junk foods.** *You will have more pennies in your pocket and the added bonus of improved health.*

It's entirely possible to eat like a king without emptying your wallet. Money saving tips for the health conscious place pennies in your pocket as you begin to eat smarter. Avoid anti-nutrient containing foods and purchase nutrient rich foods.

Prices of Common Healthy Foods

TABLE 4.1

TYPES OF FOODS	INTERESTING FACTS	EST. COST PER SERVING
BROWN RICE	Has many B vitamins	$.024
BUCKWHEAT	Not actually wheat	$.036
MILLET	Very likeable and healthy	$.014
QUINOA	High in protein	$0.47
DRY PINTO BEANS COSTCO® (25 POUNDS FOR $12.99)	Has cholesterol lowering fiber. Helps maintain blood sugar levels after eating.	$.017
EGGS (5 DOZEN FOR $6.59)	Excellent source of protein and healthy fats.	$0.22
BONELESS CHICKEN ($2.99/POUND)	Excellent source of protein, vitamins and minerals.	$0.73
CANNED SALMON (6 CANS FOR $9.99)	High in Essential Fatty Acids-Omega-3's.	$1.67
MILK (2 GALLONS FOR $6.99)	High in Calcium and Vitamin D.	$0.39
BOTTLED WATER (CASE OF 24, 16 OZ EACH)	Assists cellular homeostasis.	$0.25

Prices of Common Processed Foods

TABLE 4.2

TYPES OF FOODS	INTERESTING FACTS	EST. COST PER SERVING
BAGELS WITH PIZZA TOPPING (18 COUNT PACKAGE)	Contains bleached flour and high fructose corn syrup	$1.11
PIZZA ROLLS (40 COUNT PACKAGE)	Contains partially hydrogenated soybean oil, preservatives and additives	$0.50
CHOCOLATE CHIP COOKIES (14.9 OZ PACKAGE)	Refined sugar, partially hydrogenated soybean oil, and additives	$0.42
SODA (CASE OF 24,12 OZ CANS)	Up to 70 chemicals not listed on the labels	$0.54
SUGARED CEREAL (16.9 OZ BOX)	Refined sugar, high fructose corn syrup and preservatives	$0.25

CHAPTER *five*

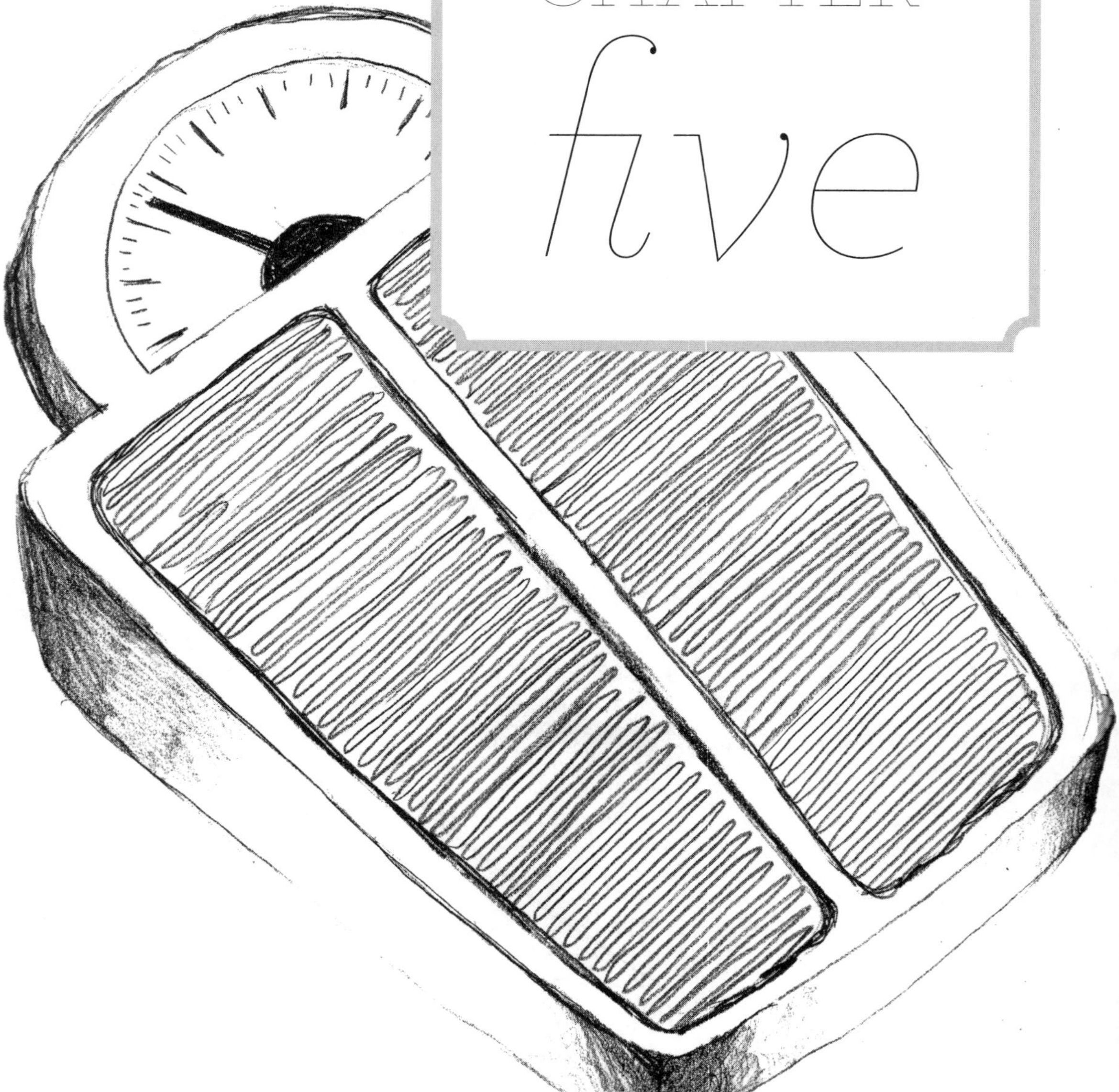

tackling weighty issues

HOW TO FIND HARMONY AND HEALTH THROUGH
NUTRITIONAL BALANCING

Is your belt a little tighter? Or perhaps some extra weight has been creeping on you for quite some time. You might be wondering why this is happening and why it's so difficult to lose weight—two of the thorniest questions for Americans today. Over recent decades, there have been profound changes in the rising epidemic of obesity and increased weight gain around the world. Despite a huge weight-loss industry, our obesity rate continues to climb. Overeating, emotional issues, metabolic dysfunctions, economic growth, modernization, urbanization and globalization of food markets are just some of the forces that underlie this worldwide epidemic.

Diets high in complex carbohydrates, lend themselves to diets with higher proportions of unhealthy fats and sugars.

Our greatest weakness lies in giving up. The most certain way to succeed is always to try just one more time.

Thomas A. Edison

At the same time, there are significant shifts towards less physical activity with increased uses of automated transport, technology and additional passive leisure activities.

Weight loss is a significant problem in our society today. Worldwide, more than one billion adults are overweight—and at least 300 million of them are clinically obese. Childhood obesity is already epidemic in some areas and on the rise in others. An estimated twenty-two million children under five are estimated to be overweight worldwide. According to the U.S. Surgeon General, in the United States, the number of overweight children has doubled and the number of overweight adolescents has tripled since 1980.

What would you attempt if you knew you could not fail?

Unknown Author

IMPACT ON HEALTH

Being overweight or obese significantly impacts your health. It leads to adverse metabolic effects on blood pressure, cholesterol, triglycerides and insulin resistance. Other health problems that are not life threatening, but associated with obesity include respiratory difficulties, chronic musculoskeletal problems, skin problems and infertility. The more life-threatening problems fall into four main areas: cardiovascular diseases; conditions associated with insulin resistance such as Type 2 diabetes; certain types of cancers, especially the hormonally related and large-bowel cancers; and gallbladder disease.

WHAT TO DO?

There are hundreds of weight loss clinics, organizations, websites and books to help you shed those extra pounds. Choosing to follow the nutritional balancing program however, allows most people to obtain a desirable weight with ease. Most weight loss programs in general tend to be dangerous, from the point of view of nutritional balancing. They either tend to starve the body, or they unbalance the body with extreme diets, too much exercise or the use of various drugs, herbs and other products that do not address the basic causes of weight gain and weight normalization.

THERE ARE VARIOUS REASONS FOR
WEIGHT GAIN:

① **Too much food**.
Many people overeat for different reasons. Some eat too much food. Others find themselves eating out of nervousness, or out of habit. Many people might eat too much food because they are trying to keep up their strength and food stimulates them in some way. Others might find themselves needing to eat more because the food they eat is of poor quality and contains few nutrients. Therefore, their body wants more food and the result is that they eat more food because they are hungry. As you eat better quality food, improve your digestion, and take the general supplements, often your appetite will decrease.

② **An improper diet.**
Eliminate poor quality foods of all kinds. The most common dietary mistake today is consuming too many carbohydrates such as breads, pizza, donuts, rolls, potato chips, pasta, soda, French fries, chocolate, cakes and candy. If you change your diet to that which consists mainly of steamed vegetables with fresh meats and whole milk dairy, weight is not usually an issue. I know what you are thinking, whole milk? Yes, a small amount of organic or raw whole milk products, eight ounces a day, is suggested.

③ **Metabolic Imbalances.**
Most people today often have underactive thyroid glands and adrenal glands and this can cause weight gain. To correct this, the basic diet and supplements in this book can be helpful. However, if this is not enough, then it is suggested that you follow a complete program, which involves a hair tissue mineral analysis with a practitioner advising you. (See www.drlwilson.com for a list of practitioners.)

④ **Many bodies today are too yin.**
This means expanded and is another cause of weight gain. The solution is the basic diet, (Table 2.3 page 56) and supplements.(See page 66) However, if this is not enough, then it is suggested that a hair tissue mineral analysis be obtained. (See www.drlwilson.com for a list of practitioners.)

⑤ **Mental/Emotional reasons for weight gain.**
Mental tension can impair nutrition and can lead to overeating of food. Some eat because they are fearful or angry. And some people eat food for emotional reasons and see food as an emotional reward.

SLOW OXIDATION & WEIGHT GAIN

Typically, those with slow oxidation gain weight on their hips and thighs resulting in a more pear-shaped body type. There are various reasons for weight gain in the slow oxidizer. They are:

- **Fatigue or depression**
  Eating to keep up their energy.

- **Low blood sugar**
  Due to weak adrenal glands, they often crave sugary foods.

- **Digestive enzymes are low**
  Can impair appetite, and also lower nutrient absorption, causing hunger for more nutrients.

- **Food sensitivities**
  Can cause bloating, gas and water retention.

- **Poor circulation**
  Can make it harder to breakdown fat deposits in the body.

- **Metal and chemical toxicity**
  The body often retains some fluid to dilute certain toxins.

FAST OXIDATION & WEIGHT GAIN

Many with fast oxidation are overweight, counterintuitive to what you might think. True fast oxidizers usually gain weight in their belly and upper body, while the legs or arms may be thin. Fast oxidizers can gain weight for many of the same reasons the slow oxidizer gains weight, such as, the desire to obtain more nutrients and food sensitivities.

ADDITIONALLY, THE FAST OXIDIZER CAN GAIN WEIGHT FOR THE FOLLOWING REASONS:

- **High cortisol level**
  Since fast oxidizers have adrenal glands that are more active, they secrete higher levels of cortisol. This higher level of cortisol, causes fat to be deposited mainly in the abdomen and sometimes in the shoulders.

- **Higher insulin**
  Fast oxidizers have higher insulin levels than slow oxidizers. Insulin tends to convert sugars to fat.

REASONS WHY A LOWER-CARBOHYDRATE DIET WORKS WELL FOR THE FAST OXIDIZER INCLUDE:

* *Eating carbohydrates increases insulin, which converts sugar to fat.*

* *Quality fats and oils provide calories and balance a fast oxidation rate.*

* *Research performed by Dr. George Watson, has shown that in fast oxidizers the Krebs cycle is more efficient than the glycolysis cycle. In the Krebs cycle, fats are converted to energy, therefore explaining why they feel better with more fats and fewer carbohydrates*

By examining the oxidation rate and eating the proper nutrient rich foods, the body will begin to make a transformation into a more balanced pattern. As this occurs, extra weight can melt away with little effort. According to Dr. Lawrence Wilson, author of *Nutritional Balancing*, (2010) "there is rarely a need for special diets, surgeries, medical drugs, bio-identical hormones or other methods that are less safe and often extremely toxic or harmful in other ways. Optimal weight can be accomplished with discipline and balancing the oxidation rate."

Try thinking of the body as though it were an orchestra. All the parts need to play in harmony for the body to function optimally. If the violin or clarinet is out of tune, there will be problems. In your body, if one mineral is out of balance, or your oxidation rate is unbalanced, it affects the whole body. By eating high quality nutrition, your body will be provided with a foundation for good health, a balanced biochemistry and your ideal weight.

Gentle rebalancing of the body chemistry, with periodic retesting, will unwind the causes of obesity.

Dr. Wilson, author of Nutritional Balancing.

SOME WEIGHT LOSS TIPS

① LOVE AND HONOR YOURSELF.

② EMPLOY HEALTHY EATING HABITS.
This includes chewing your food, eating slowly, limiting poor quality snack foods, and keeping the proper foods in the house so as to avoid situations where you might overeat.

③ CHANGE YOUR DIET.
Remove all products that are made from sugar and white flour.

④ AVOID ALL ARTIFICIAL SWEETENERS.
They tend to cause weight gain, by tricking the body into thinking a sweet meal has arrived causing the body to secrete insulin, leading to fat being stored in the body.

⑤ JOIN A WEIGHT LOSS SUPPORT GROUP.
In your community or even an online support group. It is helpful to know that others are there for moral support.

⑥ SET REALISTIC GOALS FOR YOURSELF.
Remember, slow and steady wins the race.

⑦ USE GIMMICKS.
Purchase small quantities of foods you feel you cannot live without. For instance, buy one cookie if you desire it, instead of purchasing an entire box. Another gimmick might be to buy a box of prunes and suck on the prune pit during the day so that you have a sweet taste in your mouth.

⑧ HAVE A SWEET TREAT.
If you need to, have a sweet treat. Ask a friend to come along and help support you so that you do not wind up buying a supersized dessert.

⑨ Ask the waiter to **TAKE THE BREAD OFF THE TABLE.**

⑩ **DO NOT GO TO PLACES THAT YOU ARE TEMPTED TO BREAK YOUR DIET.** Do not go out with friends that are not supportive of your health.

Instead of giving
myself reasons why
I can't, I give myself
reasons why I can.

Unknown Author

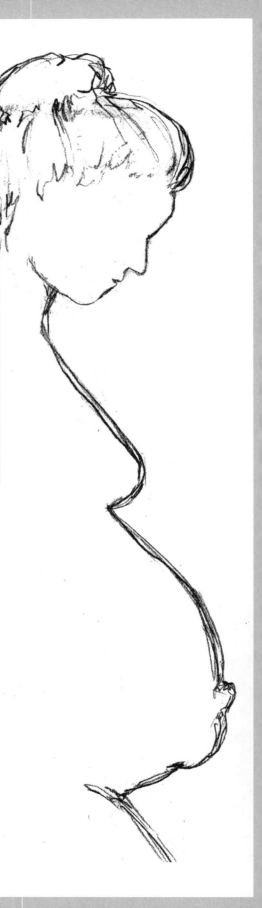

CHAPTER
six

expectant moms

OR WOMEN WHO ARE CONSIDERING PREGNANCY

"Is my baby healthy?" are usually the first words a new mother asks after she delivers her baby. If a new mom desires a healthy baby, she must examine how she takes care of her body before the baby is born; prenatal care is the first step in ensuring a baby's optimal health. However, care for both the mother and the baby begin far too late in a woman's life.

Typically, women do not begin eating well and nourishing their bodies until they learn of their pregnancy, which could be a few weeks to a few months after a missed cycle. Those early weeks of a pregnancy—the first eight to twelve weeks or the first trimester—are crucial to a baby's health since at this decisive time, key organs and tissues are being formed and developed.

Making a decision to have a child— it's momentous. It is to decide forever to have your heart go walking around outside your body.

Elizabeth Stone

This modern day approach of waiting to begin prenatal care until after conception sadly misses the mark. A woman's body needs to be nourished and adequately vital to birth a healthy child. Even when a woman learns she is pregnant, and visits her health care provider, today's medical model of prenatal care does not teach a healthful lifestyle, recommend a superb diet and rest, provide adequate supplements and encourage emotional peace. Issues surrounding and avoiding all toxic substances, contained in air, water, food, as well as products that are applied to the skin and body are not discussed either.

Women need to be educated on the fact that pregnancy is an enormous stressor on the body demanding high quality nutrition, vitamins and minerals as well as energy reserves from the body. Just imagine what the body does on a daily basis when it is not creating a new, living and breathing human being. Each day, it makes millions of red blood cells, produces multiple quarts of digestive juices to break down food that absorbs nutrients, and replaces its line of defense weekly through the immune system to maintain your health. These unseen biochemical processes are all powered by the nutrients and minerals consumed in food and water each day. Our modern day system of prenatal care does too little, too late. It's time for a change.

Instead, the cornerstone of a superb prenatal care program needs to have, as its foundation, a program that begins as early as puberty or even at birth for both sexes as several years may be necessary to improve the health of both men and women. This concept is essential so that women

can nourish their bodies adequately to ensure not only their health, but their baby's health as well. Forty or more vitamins and minerals are needed to ensure that both mother and child have strong immune systems, proper bone and brain development and a risk free birth experience. To replace one mineral can take more than nine months.

Diets of couples considering having children, should include as many mineral rich foods as possible that include, pasture raised meats and eggs, a cornucopia of steamed vegetables and healthy fats, such as butter and flax oil in their diets. (See Table 2.3 for recommended foods) These foods are important because they are rich in minerals, vitamins, proteins and fats that are essential to building and maintaining vitality.

A mother's health is vitally important to the wellness of her newborn infant, though in developed countries this does not always seems to be the case. For instance, the United States has the eighteenth highest rate for newborn mortality.[37]

A baby is something you carry inside you for nine months, in your arms for three years and in your heart till the day you die.

Mary Mason

In America, the birth-defect rate has doubled since 1950. The generations born in the wake of mass modification of food products now face record numbers of devastating conditions like: failure to thrive, autism, ADD, depression, fatigue, anxiety and a host of defects related to prescriptions as well as engineered food products. A benefit of properly interpreted hair tissue mineral analysis is that it allows women to screen for nutritional deficits and toxic metals in their systems before they conceive.[38] It also helps many women who have had trouble conceiving and carrying to term by reducing the toxic metal burden, remineralizing the body, and returning their body to its natural state of dynamic equilibrium.

Correcting mineral imbalances can make a significant difference in pregnancy and birth. Important vitamins and minerals found in whole foods promotes the healthy functioning of the biological system. Beyond prenatal issues, diseases that manifest in adulthood can often be linked to prenatal nutrition. For example, infants born at a particularly low weight have increased risk of cardiovascular disease.[39] One study showed lead, cadmium, and zinc levels in placental tissues, could be used to accurately predict the birth weight and head circumference of the newborn.[40] Therefore, if a woman is exposed to lead or cadmium, either through cigarette smoke or exhaust fumes it can affect her unborn baby's health. In conclusion, the research reported that any child born under 6.9 pounds should be tested for suboptimum nutrition. Taking care of yourself when you are expecting is imperative to help ensure a healthy baby.

Resist the temptation to eat poor quality junk food, drink alcohol and smoke cigarettes as these items damage the integrity of the cellular processes within the body and greatly increase the risk of heavy metal toxicity. (See Appendix C) Give up late nights and reduced sleep and trade them in for quality sleep. This will regenerate and heal the body. If you are thinking about getting pregnant, nutritional balancing can help you strengthen your body.

WHAT SHOULD PREGNANT WOMEN EAT, TO OPTIMIZE HER BABY'S HEALTH?

THE LIST BELOW PROVIDES EXCELLENT RECOMMENDATIONS:

①　**A large serving of steamed organic vegetables that covers ½ to ⅔ of your plate twice daily (or you can think of this as a double or triple serving).**
As your pregnancy progresses, especially in your last trimester, eating additional cooked vegetables and high quality protein is beneficial because of the rich assortment of minerals in these foods. These are especially important during pregnancy, as your body has increased demands to create another being. Feel free to indulge in a small serving of starchy vegetables such as squash, sweet potatoes and root vegetables, because these mineral rich marvels help support your body and your baby's health.

② **Ten to twelve ounces of fresh carrot juice daily.** *Feel free to add in some fresh greens, wheatgrass or ginger. Carrot juice is mineral rich in calcium, copper, magnesium, potassium, sodium, phosphorus, sulfur and iron. This juice is also excellent because it provides a readily bio-available form of calcium. While it is difficult for the human body to absorb high levels of calcium from sources such as dairy, which are pasteurized and homogenized, the calcium in fresh carrot juice recipes is easily assimilated. For those who are expecting, drinking carrot juice, as well as eating carrots, is thought to be especially beneficial for prenatal health. Furthermore, nursing moms should drink carrot juice throughout their lactation to provide quality milk for their baby. Carrot juice plays an important role in an infant's supply of Vitamin A. A seven ounce glass of carrot juice has only 50 calories, so do not worry about counting your calories with this nutritious beverage.*

③ **Three quarts of spring water.** *Essential to keep your body hydrated, this necessary liquid also provides natural properties that are never found in water that is available from municipal water supplies.*

④ **Pasture fed meats, eggs and dairy.** *Excellent sources of protein and rich in Omega-3's.*

⑤ **Legumes and beans in small quantities.**

⑥ **Wheat free grains such as quinoa or brown rice in small quantities.**

HERE ARE SEVERAL SUGGESTIONS FOR PRECONCEPTION HEALTH CARE AS WELL AS ADVICE FOR PREGNANT WOMEN:

- **Choose grass-fed meats, organic vegetables, and wheat-free grains.**

- **Reduce or eliminate caffeine** *as research shows (New York Times, Pregnancy Problems Tied to Caffeine, January 2008) that too much caffeine during pregnancy may increase your risk of miscarriage. Caffeine also can increase your blood pressure and heart rate within a few minutes of consumption and can even trigger heartburn.*

- **Avoid alcohol and recreational drugs** *as well as over-the-counter medicines as these substances can harm the unborn child possibly causing birth defects.*

- **Avoid extreme diets** *as they can unbalance biochemistry and fail to provide enough nutrient rich foods to ensure a healthy pregnancy.*

It is time for a new woman's paradigm, an ethic that warrants excellent care be taken of your body when you are young, so that when you are older, you will have healthy children.

- **Take recommended nutritional supplements** *such as those suggested by nutritional balancing science.*

- **Pregnant women should not keep toxic cleaning supplies, insecticides, pesticides, toxic paints, and other toxic materials in their home** *as they can irritate the eyes, skin and lungs as well as cause birth defects or even cancer for your unborn child. Research in Britain showed that households that used toxic cleaning supplies during pregnancy were twice as likely to have children with asthma. The National Institute of Health has a site where you can check the safety and toxicity information on each product. Their link is http://hpd.nlm.nih.gov/index. htm. In lieu of toxic cleaning products, try cleaning with lemon juice which is a disinfectant and grease cutter, white vinegar, also cuts grease, and liquid soaps such as castile that also cleans. Borax®, too, is an excellent disinfectant while baking soda also cleans and deodorizes.*

- **Live clean and natural.** *Choose soaps, shampoos, lotion hair dyes and sprays that minimize health issues. (See this website for toxic free products www. cosmeticsdatabase.com for a review of over 25,000 products). Skin care, hair and body products that are mass-produced today are often filled with toxic ingredients that are linked to infertility and breast cancer. Moreover, "researchers have detected a total of 287 chemicals in the cord blood of Newborns (Red Cross, EWG, 2004) including chemicals that cause cancer and are toxic to the brain and nervous system."*

- **Exercise lightly** *like walking or yoga. Childbirth is physically demanding.*

- **Get plenty of sleep and rest** *to regenerate the body.*

- **Learn to meditate and minimize stress.** *This can relax the mind and body, which is helpful to both mother and child.*

- **Avoid sugar, artificial sweeteners, preservatives or chemical additives.**

- **Minimize electromagnetic disturbances** *(EMF's): limit cell phones, computers and other electronic devices as research shows an increased risk of miscarriages. Moreover, according to a recent study, (O. Johansson, Disturbance of the immune system by electromagnetic fields- A potentially underlying cause for cellular damage and tissue repair reduction which could lead to disease and impairment, Pathophysiology (2009)) in both "human and animal, large immunological changes upon exposure to environmental levels of modern human-made EMFs" were found. These EMFs can cause significant changes in cells, indicating an increase in allergic responses and inflammatory conditions as well as an increased cancer risk.*

CHAPTER
seven

healthy children

Taking excellent care of our young ones is one of the best gifts a parent can give a child. It's important to select the best foods for a growing child and to understand that children have needs that are quite different from those of their parents. Healthy children have a greater chance for a healthy adult life. In addition, tastes, preferences and eating habits begin during childhood and affect the choices made as an adult.

Food preparation at home is an opportunity to teach our children and have fun with them as well. When children feel a part of the process, they are more likely to try new foods. I often let my children thumb through cookbook recipes and have them pick out what they like.

Please understand my friend, that where you find yourself tomorrow is a function of the positive decisions and actions you take today.

Akin A. Waialua

The use of hair tissue mineral analysis and nutritional balancing can help parents learn more about their children's nutritional needs and deficits. Detecting requirements at an early age helps youngsters achieve optimal health—both body and mind—during childhood, and determine the quality of life for years to come. While most of the same principles outlined earlier apply here, children and infants have certain needs that must be considered. Food choices for children should take into consideration very specific requirements.

HAIR TISSUE MINERAL ANALYSIS FOR CHILDREN

Hair tissue mineral analysis can help determine the best foods for your child. One of the benefits of this test is determining your child's oxidation level and preparing meals according to their oxidation type.

FAST OXIDATION & CHILDREN

Most young children are fast oxidizers. Young children in particular fall into this category that ranges from birth to about four years old. Children who are fast oxidizers need healthy fats; they are an integral part of the fast oxidizer diet. These healthy fats include: Omega-3 fatty acids, flaxseed oil, raw olive oil, cod liver oil, full fat organic certified raw dairy, eggs, natural and grass fed meats, and nut butters. Parents should not be concerned that healthy fat is harmful to their child. In fact, the opposite is true.

A diet rich in good quality fats and oils are necessary for the fast oxidizer child because:

- *Fat slows down the metabolic rate bringing the body into a more stabilized, balanced energy pattern.*

- *Fat provides extra calories that many fast oxidizers need to maintain their energy.*

- *Fat is digested slowly and provides a continuous supply of energy to stabilize blood sugar.*

- *Essential fatty acids are vital for optimal brain development.*

Sugar is one of the worst foods for fast oxidizers. Omitting healthful fats and oils from your child's diet is an enormous mistake. Without them, a fast oxidizer will crave sweets, starting a cycle of rapidly fluctuating blood sugar levels. Eating too much sugar and starch is the main cause of obesity in children. Children who are deprived of the necessary fats and oils are likely to demonstrate behavioral issues as well as health problems. Remember that young children do not have the same nutritional needs or limitations as adults.

A WORD ON KIDS SUPPLEMENTS

When children are small, it is necessary to grind up the vitamins or crush them with a pill crusher because they cannot swallow large pills. Once you grind up the pills, mix them into a food such as almond butter, yogurt, tomato sauce or even applesauce if necessary. Another option is to place the vitamins into a blender with some whole milk and yogurt. When your children are able to swallow supplements, watch them take their vitamins so they do not throw them away.

FEEDING BABIES

When a baby comes into the world, you want to give him or her the best nutrition possible. In regards to milk, breast milk as opposed to formula is the best choice available because it is easily digestible, allowing for optimum assimilation of nutrients. Mother's breast milk offers the perfect combination of proteins, fats, carbohydrates, vitamins, minerals and water. It is best if a woman can breast feed for the first 2-3 years of their child's life so that the nutrient rich breast milk optimizes the baby's health.

If breastfeeding is not a viable option for you, try a natural formula. The Weston Price Foundation has three wonderful options available:

1. RAW MILK BABY FORMULA
(*See page 102*)

2. GOAT MILK BABY FORMULA
(*See page 103*)

3. LIVER-BASED BABY FORMULA
(*See page 104*)

RAW MILK BABY FORMULA

Weston Price's milk-based formula takes into account the fact that human milk is richer in whey, lactose, vitamin C, niacin, and long-chain polyunsaturated fatty acids compared to cow's milk but leaner in casein (milk protein). The addition of gelatin to cow's milk formula will make it more digestible for the infant. Use only truly expeller-expressed oils in the formula recipes, otherwise they may lack vitamin E.

The ideal milk-based formula for baby, if he/she cannot be breastfed, is clean, whole raw milk from old-fashioned cows, certified free of disease that feed on green pasture. For sources of good quality milk, see www.realmilk.com or contact a local chapter of the Weston A. Price Foundation.

If the only choice available to you for preparation of a formula is commercial milk, choose whole milk, preferably organic and non-homogenized, and culture it with a piima or kefir culture to restore enzymes. (available from G.E.M. Cultures 253-588-2922 or http://www.gemcultures.com).

To enjoy good health, to bring true happiness to one's family, to bring peace to all, one must first discipline and control one's mind.

Buddha

RECIPE FOR RAW MILK BABY FORMULA

Makes 36 ounces.

INGREDIENTS

2 cups whole raw cow's milk, preferably from pasture-fed cows

¼ cup homemade liquid whey
(See recipe for whey, below)
NOTE: DO NOT use powdered whey or whey from making cheese (which will cause the formula to curdle). Use only homemade whey made from yoghurt, kefir or separated raw milk.

4 tablespoons lactose[1]

¼ teaspoon bifidobacterium infantis[2]

2 or more tablespoons good quality cream (preferably not ultrapasteurized), more if you are using milk from Holstein cows

½ teaspoon unflavored high-vitamin or high-vitamin fermented cod liver oil or 1 teaspoon regular cod liver oil[3]

¼ teaspoon high-vitamin butter oil (optional)[1]

1 teaspoon expeller-expressed sunflower oil[1]

1 teaspoon extra virgin olive oil[1]

2 teaspoons coconut oil[1]

2 teaspoons Frontier™ nutritional yeast flakes[1]

2 teaspoons gelatin[1]

1⅞ cups filtered water

¼ teaspoon acerola powder [1,2]

INSTRUCTIONS

(1) Put 2 cups filtered water into a Pyrex® measuring pitcher and remove 2 tablespoons (that will give you 1⅞ cups water).

(2) Pour about half of the water into a pan and place on a medium flame.

(3) Add the gelatin and lactose to the pan and let dissolve, stirring occasionally.

(4) When the gelatin and lactose are dissolved, remove from heat and add the remaining water to cool the mixture.

(5) Stir in the coconut oil and optional high-vitamin butter oil and stir until melted.

(6) Meanwhile, place remaining ingredients into a blender.

(7) Add the water mixture and blend about three seconds.

(8) Place in glass bottles or a glass jar and refrigerate.

(9) Before giving to baby, warm bottles by placing in hot water or a bottle warmer. NEVER warm bottles in a microwave oven. (A microwave oven heats unevenly, basically from the inside out, so it's possible that the formula could be very hot in the middle of the bottle but barely lukewarm on the outside where you can feel it.)

VARIATION:
GOAT MILK FORMULA

Although goat milk is rich in fat, it must be used with caution in infant feeding as it lacks folic acid and is low in vitamin B12, both of which are essential to the growth and development of the infant. Inclusion of nutritional yeast to provide folic acid is essential. To compensate for low levels of vitamin B12, if preparing the Milk-Based Formula (above) with goat's milk, add 2 teaspoons organic raw chicken liver, frozen for 14 days, finely grated to the batch of formula. Be sure to begin egg-yolk feeding at four months.

SOURCES

1. Available from Radiant Life
   888-593-8333, www.radiantlifecatalog.com

2. Use only recommended brands of cod liver oil:

   Green Pasture Products: Blue Ice High-Vitamin Fermented Cod Liver Oil, (402) 858-4818, green-pasture.org

   Dr. Ron's Ultra-Pure: Blue Ice High-Vitamin Fermented Cod Liver Oil, (877) 472-8701, drrons.com

   Radiant Life: Blue Ice High-Vitamin Fermented Cod Liver Oil and Premier High-Vitamin Cod Liver Oil, (888) 593-8333, 4radiantlife.com

   Azure Standard: Blue Ice High-Vitamin Fermented Cod Liver Oil, (541) 467-2230, azurestandard.com

   Natural Health Advocates: Blue Ice High-Vitamin Fermented Cod Liver Oil, 888-257-8775, building-health.com/

LET'S GET COOKING

In our household, everyone is included in meal preparation. I find this helpful because it exposes everyone to a variety of different types of food. Children can help create new recipes at mealtime by allowing them to participate in the process. It will also raise your awareness about their preferences. Planning out meals ahead of time is essential. Hungry teenagers won't always wait for that well-balanced meal to finish cooking. Planning is key if you want healthy children. It's a good idea to prepare enough to assure leftovers will be available in the fridge when your hungry kids get home from school or activities. Quality protein, fats, and lots of vegetables strengthen their bodies and help them grow into vibrant young adults.

Children can be notoriously picky eaters. By letting them have input in the kitchen, you're likely to have better success when dinner is on the table. I created a children's section in my cookbook in response to the many questions and suggestions from my clients. Nutrient rich dishes are as essential as ever, given the physical and emotional stresses that face our children every day. Moreover, parents are competing with a perpetual onslaught of advertisements for foods that have a shockingly low nutritional value but rate high in flashy commercial and seductive packaging. Countless snack foods advertise bogus health benefits, from so-called vitamin drinks to energy bars.

Despite all the knowledge we have about health and nutrition, young people demonstrate an astounding number of illnesses, many of which are directly traceable to their diets. Years ago, it was rare to find

RECIPE FOR LIVER-BASED FORMULA

Makes 36 ounces.

Our liver-based formula also mimics the nutrient profile of mother's milk. It is extremely important to include coconut oil in this formula as it is the only ingredient that provides the special medium-chain saturated fats found in mother's milk. As with the milk-based formula, all oils should be truly expeller-expressed.

INGREDIENTS

3¾ cups homemade beef or chicken broth

2 ounces organic liver, cut into small pieces

5 tablespoons lactose[1]

¼ teaspoon bifidobacterium infantis[2]

¼ cup homemade liquid whey
(See recipe for whey, below)

1 tablespoon coconut oil[1]

½ teaspoon unflavored high-vitamin or high-vitamin fermented cod liver oil or 1 teaspoon regular cod liver oil[3]

1 teaspoon unrefined sunflower oil[1]

2 teaspoons extra virgin olive oil[1]

¼ teaspoon acerola powder[1,2]

INSTRUCTIONS

① Simmer liver gently in broth until the meat is cooked through.

② Liquefy using a handheld blender or in a food processor.

③ When the liver broth has cooled, stir in remaining ingredients.

④ Store in a very clean glass or stainless steel container.

To serve, stir formula well and pour 6 to 8 ounces in a very clean glass bottle. Attach a clean nipple and set in a pan of simmering water until formula is warm but not hot to the touch, shake well and feed to baby. Never heat formula in a microwave oven! (A microwave oven heats unevenly, basically from the inside out, so it's possible that the formula could be very hot in the middle of the bottle but barely lukewarm on the outside where you can feel it.)

It's bizarre that the produce manager is more important to my children's health than the pediatrician.

Meryl Streep

degenerative diseases among the young. Today it's appallingly common. Arthritis, epilepsy, multiple sclerosis, and diabetes strike youngsters at a high rate. Approximately seven million young people a year are afflicted with learning issues such as ADD and ADHD.[41] Autism is at an all time high in this nation and considered to be at epidemic proportions.[42] Drug resistant viruses, chemical sensitivities, and problems with immune system now affect both young and old. While poor prenatal care might account for a number of these maladies, there is little doubt that the surplus of high sugar, empty calorie, and nutrient–free concoctions have had an enormously negative impact on American health.

SOURCES

1. Available from Radiant Life
   888-593-8333, www.radiantlifecatalog.com

2. Use only recommended brands of cod liver oil:

   Green Pasture Products: Blue Ice High-Vitamin Fermented Cod Liver Oil, (402) 858-4818, green-pasture.org

   Dr. Ron's Ultra-Pure: Blue Ice High-Vitamin Fermented Cod Liver Oil, (877) 472-8701, drrons.com

   Radiant Life: Blue Ice High-Vitamin Fermented Cod Liver Oil and Premier High-Vitamin Cod Liver Oil, (888) 593-8333, 4radiantlife.com

   Azure Standard: Blue Ice High-Vitamin Fermented Cod Liver Oil, (541) 467-2230, azurestandard.com

   Natural Health Advocates: Blue Ice High-Vitamin Fermented Cod Liver Oil, 888-257-8775, building-health.com/

LET'S COOK SOMETHING UP

Please consider the importance of getting back into the kitchen. It does not mean that you need to spend long hours cooking. But it does mean that you need to spend some time preparing and cooking food with wisdom so you create the healthiest options for your family. Try to establish who will prepare food. If no one has time, as a family, rethink your schedule because there is no other way to feed kids quality foods other than rediscovering your kitchen and cooking wholesome meals.

When you cook your own meals, you know what is in your food. Cooking your own meals helps to guarantee that your foods come from the earth without any unhealthy additives. Preparing and cooking real whole foods is a necessary step to improved vitality. It's time to slow down, get back into the kitchen, and cook meals that foster health.

FOOD GLORIOUS FOOD...

Once your baby shows an interest in table food, the best food is fresh, homemade baby food given its wonderful and superior flavor. Would you rather eat a fresh carrot or a canned carrot? The former tastes juicy and sweet, bursting with flavor, while the later tastes similar to flavored cardboard. Remember, canned vegetables can have a shelf life of two years. So while it is sitting in the can for this period of time, its taste and nutritional value are negatively affected. It's no wonder that kids do not like the taste of vegetables. Babies, just like adults, enjoy the delicious smells, vivid colors, and vibrant tastes of foods and their delectable aromas.

Even though it may be hard for you to find the time to make homemade baby food, it is hands down the best choice for your growing tot. Loaded with more nutrients than store bought baby food it contains many vitamins and minerals that are not present in jarred baby foods. Moreover, water and air are put into the commercially jarred baby foods to give them a fluffy, smooth texture, while consequently minimizing the vitamin and mineral content. If you have the time to make your own food, you can avoid the sugars, fillers, artificial colors, additives, and preservatives. Instead, get the simple pure taste of clean food, with all of the nutrients intact. Please remember, this is a short-term project; children soon will be eating wholesome whole foods.

The order of baby food preference that is recommended is:

① Homemade organic baby food: *(Food can be puréed in a blender, food processor, small electric chopper or a simple baby food grinder.) Extra food can be frozen in ice cube trays or stored in Glad® Freezer Bags. (This brand does not release chemicals into the foods.)*

② Organic store bought baby food

③ Frozen baby food

④ Name brand baby food

In the first years of your child's life, excellent nutrition is critical for his/her development and health. There is no other time where nutrition plays such an important role in a child's life. Babies will triple their birth weight and by age three they will have doubled their height. Throughout this period, twenty teeth will begin to show, babies will learn to walk, talk and feed themselves; and brain growth will be unsurpassed at any other time in their lives.[43] Therefore, what you feed your children will enable them to develop into healthy adults.

Clearly, nutrition is critical to the vibrant health and development of children. As infants continue to grow and develop into more mature children, do not forget they need healthy, nutrient rich foods because it will optimize their health. Make sure to take time to prepare healthy meats, steam and purée a wide variety of organic vegetables, and provide healthy fats for your growing child.

Please follow the Nutritional Balancing Food Recommendations for children as suggested in Table 2.3.

OPERATION COVERT VEGETABLES AND HEALTHY IDEAS

You might be thinking, "How do I get my child to eat all of these new recommended foods?" Go slowly and introduce these items to your child in a fun and creative way. You might say to him or her, "We're going to try some new recipes today, come and help me." You'll be surprised by how eager children will be to dive in and help cook with you after enthusiastically introducing them to cooking. They'll soon be found putting their fingers into the new foods and tasting them as you prepare these new dishes.

If a woman could see the sparks of light going forth from her fingertips when she is cooking, and the substance of light that goes into the food she handles, she would be amazed to see how much of herself she charges into the meals that she prepares for her family and friends. It is one of the most important and least understood activities of life that the radiation and feelings that go into the preparation of food affect everyone who partakes of it. And this activity should be unhurried, peaceful, and happy because the substance of the lifestream performing the service flows into that food and is eaten, and actually becomes part of the energy of the receiver. It would be better that an individual did not eat at all than to eat food that has been prepared under a feeling of anger, apathy, resentment, depression, or any outward pressure.

Maha Chohan, Electrons

Another option for those finicky eaters is to hide your new items. This is where Operation Covert Vegetables comes into action. According to the dictionary, covert means not openly acknowledged or displayed, so when your children are not in the kitchen with you, add in different puréed or shredded vegetables into their foods. For any type of meat dish, try adding in cauliflower purée or carrot purée. For a dish that calls for pasta, try this sly substitution, spaghetti squash. Looks like pasta, but has minimal carbohydrates and is packed with nutrient rich minerals. If you do not have time to purée the vegetables, go ahead and purchase jars of baby food, preferably organic brands. I know that it is not always feasible to have freshly puréed vegetables prepared. So go ahead, stuff the purée inside meatballs, meatloaves, burgers and chili dishes—your covert operation will go surprisingly smoothly.

FOOD ALLERGIES

Food allergies and food sensitivities are often not understood or given the recognition they deserve today. They are important to consider as certain foods, such as wheat and cow's milk can trigger a variety of health issues. This is a very important area for children and adults.

Causes for food sensitivities include:

- **Being fatigued and then eating a meal when you are tired** *can trigger food reactions. In order to digest food, energy is required.*

- **Certain foods such as wheat, beef, unfermented soy products and commercially grown dairy products** *are no longer healthful for anyone due to genetic modification, hybridization of seeds and poor farming practices.*

- **Disturbed digestion, leaky gut syndrome** *(Leaky gut syndrome refers to excessive permeability of the intestinal tract. This allows partially digested food and other harmful chemicals to be absorbed into the blood stream, resulting in allergic reactions) and deficiencies of digestive enzymes causes food allergies in many young children and adults.*

- **Stress and poor eating habits** *(such as eating too much, not chewing thoroughly or not resting after meals can cause food reactions) can shut down the digestive system, allowing food that has not been fully digested to pass to the intestines, irritating this organ.*

- **Foods that are processed in an unhealthy way or cooked improperly** *can cause food allergies. For example, homogenization, pasteurization, milling, grinding, and fermentation alter components of the foods and may cause a reaction.*

- **Food additives,** *which include artificial colors, enhancers, flavors, and emulsifiers are neurotoxins that can trigger an allergic reaction in the body.*

- **Too many foods combined together** *can cause reactions for those people who have weakened digestion.*[44]

ELIMINATING CERTAIN FOODS

To avoid food reactions, eliminate all products made with wheat, most beef and most non-organic dairy products except butter. A small amount of tofu and tempeh should be okay for most people. Reasons for these specific food eliminations are that:

1. *Today, hybrid wheat flour is comprised of approximately 33 percent glutamic acid, an inflammatory amino acid.*

2. *Wheat, along with other grains, stimulates insulin production, which also increases inflammation.*

3. *Additionally, wheat and other grains are high in Omega-6 fatty acids, which are pro-inflammatory. This often aggravates the intestines, producing leaky gut syndrome that may then cause more food reactions.*

4. *Cow's milk dairy products are another common cause of food reactions. Today they are fed corn, an unnatural food for cows. As a result, the milk and meat are high in Omega-6 fatty acids and low in Omega-3 fatty acids. This can lead to inflammation.*

5. *Also, corn-fed cows often develop intestinal infections that must be treated with antibiotics. These medicines can be traced to the milk and meat, causing reactions in sensitive people.*

6. *While tofu and tempeh are traditionally prepared soy foods, isolated soy protein, found in textured vegetable protein, protein powder, bars and many other foods, is a highly processed product more likely to cause reactions.*

If you suspect food allergies in a child follow these suggestions:

- **Feed children a diet of rice, turkey ands simple vegetables** *like broccoli and green beans (foods that are not common allergic foods) for a week and notice if the child's symptoms improve. Then slowly re-introduce other foods, noting any changes in behavior or other symptoms. This plan is most easily done with very small children and those who are not fussy about food.*

- **Go to a doctor for food allergy testing.** *Food allergy tests are not 100 percent accurate, but they can help pinpoint foods that are causing reactions. All autistic, ADD, ADHD, and developmentally delayed children should be tested for food allergies because certain foods can often be a trigger in these health conditions.*[45,46]

- **Get a Pulse Rate Test.** *Dr. Arthur Coca, an immunologist, discovered that when people eat foods to which they are allergic, the heartbeat increases by 20 beats per minute above the normal level. This finding is surprising because pulse rate is normally remarkably stable, not affected by digestion, or ordinary physical activities, or normal emotions. Therefore, unless a person is ill or under great stress, pulse rate deviation when eating is probably due to allergies. By performing this test, one can find and eliminate foods that trigger allergies.*

SUGGESTIONS AND GUIDELINES FOR HEALTHY CHILDREN

Over the years, I have made family mealtime a pleasant part of the day because food plays an important role in connecting family members with one another. However, please do not pay attention to those family members and friends that pressure you into feeling that your child is being deprived of certain sweet treats. Even though this might be difficult, stand your ground concerning this issue and remember that you are protecting your child's health.

On the other hand, do not try to persuade others to adopt your healthy lifestyle. With time you will learn that most people are attached to their poor food habits, even if they are ill. Remember you are providing your wee ones with a greater chance of living a life filled with optimal health. Focus on yourself and your family and put your energy into those who can benefit from this program. If you are questioned incessantly about why you or your family members are not eating certain foods, for example sugar and wheat, simply state that you are allergic. Lastly, remember that part of healing the body, is staying calm emotionally, as well as eating honest wholesome food. Most people feel that arguing about their point of view is not relaxing. The best option is to overlook unpleasant remarks others make and focus on your family's good health habits. Here are some ideas to help you get started when making healthier choices and changing your lifestyle routines.

Changing our diet is something we choose to do, not something we are forced to do. Instead of dreading it, try saying, "Here's another thing I get to do to help myself. Great!"

HERE ARE SOME IDEAS TO HELP YOU GET STARTED:

1. Explain and teach children why nutrition matters. Discuss the importance of healthy eating habits.

2. Set a good example for your children by making excellent food choices. Eat the same healthy foods, go to sleep early and try living the same lifestyle you recommend to your children.

3. Don't give into guilt, societal pressures and don't feed your child a suboptimal diet.

4. Motivate your child to improve their diet and to make better food choices. For example, teach them that good nutrition will help them have bigger muscles, shinier hair, longer nails, and much more energy. With good nutrition, kids will have more energy, which in turn will increase their self-esteem and confidence.

5. Many parents have asked me what to do when their children are with their friends. Try to teach them to make healthy choices. The best approach is to educate your children so that when you are not around they will make good choices. Also teach your children to pay attention to how they feel after they make poor food choices. This will help them see the connection between food and good health.

6. This is important! Speak up to school authorities about the amount of sugar and candy being given out by teachers during the day as a reward. Speak to the administrators about removing vending machines filled with junky foods and drinks and replace them with bottled water and healthy snacks. In Wisconsin, one high school decided to replace all junk food with healthy foods. It has been reported that there were improvements in the childrens' behavior and in their grades.[47]

7. Birthday parties can be healthful too! One year we had a cooking party. Both teams came up with a full course of healthy meals. Believe it or not, the children had fun cooking and creating nutritious meals too!

8. Avoid buying candy, cookies, donuts, ice cream and other sugary products. It will be easier for kids if the cupboards are filled with healthy choices, not sugar-coated treats. Keep the fridge filled with delicious vegetables and dips and don't forget the blue corn chips.

(9) *Play relaxing music when eating and even light some dinner candles. This type of ambiance at mealtime can really change the way everyone treats each other, which will not only ease digestion, but also enhance assimilation of essential nutrients. The kids could even help make the candles(visit http://www.care2.com/greenliving/simple-beeswax-candles-to-make-with-kids.html), Beeswax is free from dangerous chemicals, so enjoy burning these as you dine.*

(10) *Mealtimes should involve positive conversations. Do not use mealtimes to heavily criticize your child because stress will hamper digestion.*

(11) *Give all children, along with other members of the family, 2-10 ounces of carrot juice each day. You may even want to add in some celery. This can help your child obtain the minerals they need for their health. Best to drink this first thing in the morning as it is most readily absorbed on an empty stomach.*

For Infants & Toddlers—Babies should be breast fed for a year or more.

(12) *Make a family decision to have dinner at home. Use your crock-pot or cook a family meal together. Let your kids pick out a recipe they like. If they are too young to cook alone, have them cook alongside you, sampling the different tastes of the food that is being prepared. Purchase cooking aprons and maybe even a chef's hat for each child and have them decorate them with colored markers. At mealtime, try to have your child talk about the positive things that happened during his or her day.*

(13) *Join a Community Supported Agriculture Group (CSA)—this is a means to develop a relationship with a farm and also receive fresh produce weekly. Some CSA's also might ask that members work a small number of hours at the farm during the growing season. If you choose, your family can take part in farm life and harvest vegetables. This is always fun for children and their parents. You may even want to look into a summer camp that teaches organic farming. My son has gone to a farm camp for six summers and has had many positive experiences. It has also taught him the connection between organically grown foods and good health.*

(14) Take your children to the supermarket with a pre-made shopping list and have them pick out healthy foods. Have your kids look into other people's cart and see what they are choosing. Does that parent pushing the cart look healthy?

(15) Do not reward children with candy! It teaches them that receiving a sugary treat is synonymous with being good.

(16) Limit how long your child sits in front of the television as advertising conditions children to value unhealthy foods.

(17) Plant herbs such as basil, rosemary, parsley and thyme in your garden or a window planter and ask children to collect it for cooking.

(18) Do your best not to feed kids when they are totally hyped up or exhausted. Let them rest for about 15 minutes before you attempt mealtime so that digestion is optimized.

(19) Always offer a few different food choices when possible.

(20) Watch out for health food store boxed items. Most are made with sugars and fruit juices. Be careful to always read labels and not assume that they are healthy just because they are in a Health Food Store. Make sure that the food is free from sugar, artificial colors, and preservatives. Be a wise consumer and check those labels!

> A new baby is like the beginning of all things—wonder, hope, a dream of possibilites.
>
> *Eda J. Le Shan*

(21) When children try a new food and they do not like it, respond in a way that encourages them to try it again later. For example "that's ok, it's great that you tried something new. I guess you're not old enough or big enough or strong enough to enjoy that yet." They all want to get older, bigger and stronger. When they relate eating healthy foods to getting what they want, they will be more apt to try them again and again. Each new food added to their repertoire can be celebrated as an accomplishment.

Making healthy food choices for your family and the manner in which you prepare your food, is critical to their good health. Keep your recipes simple and enjoy the natural flavors of your food. Your infant, toddler, elementary aged school child, preteen or adolescent will then reap the benefits of good health.

CHAPTER

eight

kitchen organization 101

HOW TO ORGANIZE YOURSELF, SHOP, & PREPARE YOUR KITCHEN.

Does your pantry have three half full bottles of rancid vegetable oils? Partially opened bags of chips and cookies? Don't be intimated by the task at hand. Remove those partially and seldom-used items from your cupboards and countertops. Slowly begin to replace those unhealthy, partially opened, processed foods with healthier choices. You are now one step closer to an important secret to nutritional success—planning and organizing your food and cookware.

SOME SUGGESTIONS INCLUDE THE FOLLOWING:

- *Equip your kitchen with the proper appliances.*

- *Make sure your refrigerator, freezer and cupboards are stocked with appropriate ingredients and goods.*

WHERE TO SHOP

I recommend that most people find local markets that have quality organic produce, meats, eggs and whole grains. I would also suggest local farmer's markets or even Community Supported Agriculture Organizations. Most markets today have health food sections that carry many wonderful selections. Another suggestion, avoid going to the market hungry! It will often cause you to over shop for items you do not need or want. Lastly, do your best to shop on the outside aisles of the market. That is generally where the healthiest foods are located.

BEST METHODS

There are various types of cooking methods that can be used in the kitchen. All methods of cooking help breakdown food for easier assimilation. Nutritional balancing recommends the following cooking suggestions for optimal health.

steaming

Uses the steam from boiling water to cook foods. It brings out the flavors of each vegetable and involves a short cooking time.

HOW TO STEAM:

① Place ½ to 1 inch of water in a pot. Bring to a boil.

② Place vegetables in steamer basket. Lower heat and cover.

③ Steam the vegetables so that they become tender.

④ The leftover cooking water contains many vitamins and minerals and can be used by either drinking or for preparation of other foods.

HELPFUL HINTS:

• Vegetables will cook more quickly if you cut them into small pieces or slices.

• Small squashes and string beans can be steamed whole.

• Feel free to serve as a side, nut butters, sauces, or pesto sauce for your steamed vegetables.

stir-frying

A quick method used to cook foods in a wok or skillet on high heat with a moderate amount of oil. Foods are moved briskly in the pan so they are coated and cooked on all sides. This method seals in the juices and keeps the colors bright. Make sure to heat the oil before adding in the food.

sautéing

A quick method that cooks foods in an uncovered skillet using oil to seal in the tastes of foods.

HOW TO SAUTÉ:

① *Heat a skillet with a small amount of oil. High heat should be used.*

② *Add vegetables and stir with a large wooden spoon.*

③ *Cover and let cook for about 10 minutes.*

④ *When veggies are done cooking, season with some San-J® Organic, Tamari soy sauce and cover for a minute so that the flavors blend.*

crock-pot

This cookware item is well known as one of the best time saving appliances for families on the go. Also, beginner cooks love this item because all you need to do is fill it and turn it on. A couple of hours later, you will have a delicious meal that's ready to eat.

HOW TO USE:

① *Only fill the crock-pot one half to two thirds full. The foods will not cook properly if the appliance is filled to the brim.*

② *If the food and liquid level is lower, the foods will cook too quickly.*

③ *Foods cooked on the bottom of the crock-pot, cook faster so make sure your items are distributed evenly in the cooker.*

pressure cooking

Concentrates nutrients and cooks food quickly saving time and energy.

HOW TO USE:

① *Bring a few tablespoons of water to a boil, uncovered in a pressure cooker.*

② *Put in vegetables. Cover and raise up the pressure.*

③ *Reduce heat to low and cook for a short period – or remove from heat.(Cooking time varies with different vegetables.)*

④ *Cool down immediately and place pressure cooker under cold water*

⑤ *Remove vegetables at once.*

ACCEPTABLE METHODS

BAKING
A simple method of food preparation that uses dry heat in a ventilated space to cook foods thoroughly. This method enhances flavor, and reduces moisture.

GRILLING
This method is quick and tasty. When you grill your foods, it requires less cooking time, due to the high heat, than in the oven or on a stovetop.

BROILING
Quick cooking, at high temp and dry heat. The food cooks in its own juices, but the moisture is reduced.

ROASTING
This form of cooking uses dry heat, which develops an assortment of flavors and aromas.

TOASTING
This method coaxes the flavors out of foods. Examples include toasted almonds, or even toasted spices.

FERMENTING
This method of preserving foods is done through lacto-fermentation. Lactic acid is a natural preservative that stops putrefying bacteria. The starches and sugars are converted into lactic acid by the different types of lactic acid producing bacteria, lactobacilli. The growth of lactobacilli on foods helps improve their digestibility and increases vitamin levels. (Ex. yogurt, cheese, saukerkraut)

UNACCEPTABLE

DEEP-FRYING
The deep frying method is not reccommended especially when the oil is old as used by many chain restaurants.

Do not let what you cannot do interfere with what you can do.

Author unknown.

PREPARATION TO MAKE MEALTIMES EASY

① Buy several pounds of ground meats. For example, ground turkey or ground lamb. Divide up the meat and place in zip top bags (Glad® bags do not release chemicals into the foods) plastic wrap in 4-6 ounce portions. You can do the same with your chicken/turkey breasts and thighs. Place these meats in your refrigerator the night before to defrost. That way, when you come home from a long day or if you are just too tired, you have your ready sized meal portion.

RECOMMENDATIONS FOR QUICK CLEAN UP

- Submerge cookware in warm soapy water and rinse with cool water.

- Purchase non-toxic liquid soaps such as Seventh Generation™ or Mrs. Meyer's®.

- Purchase only natural brushes to clean cookware.

- For burned food stuck on bottom of pans, add water and baking soda.

FOOD STORAGE: A NOTE ON VEGETABLES

Almost all vegetables, with the exception of sweet potatoes and winter squash should be stored in the refrigerator. Air, light and heat deplete vegetables of vital nutrients. Raw vegetables, which are kept at room temperature for three days, can lose up to 70 percent of folic acid. However, when these delightful delicacies are stored in the refrigerator, they lose little or no folic acid after two weeks.

② Buy several different types of frozen vegetables to keep in your freezer. This way you are not running around at the last minute, foraging through the supermarkets looking for vegetables for dinner. Stocking the freezer with frozen vegetables will enable you to make your day simpler and easier.

③ Keep your refrigerator stocked well.

④ Always have your cupboards stocked well with helpful ingredients.

⑤ Plan out your meals for the week. *(See shopping list on page 220 to take with you to the market).*

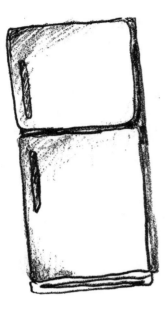

WHAT TO STOCK IN YOUR
SPICE RACK

(Non-irridated & preferably organic)

- Basil
- Cilantro
- Cinnamon
- Cumin
- Curry powder
- Dill
- Garlic
- Oregano
- Paprika
- Poppy seeds
- Rosemary
- Sea Salt
- Tarragon
- Thyme
- Turmeric

WHAT TO STOCK IN YOUR
REFRIGERATOR

- Assorted vegetables
- Assorted meats
- Eggs
- Yogurt
- Cheese
- Assorted nuts and seeds, such as almond butter, cashew butter, sunflower seed butter and sesame seed butter (tahini)
- Berries: If not in season, try frozen- no sugar added
- Butter
- Corn tortillas

WHAT TO STOCK IN YOUR
PANTRY

- Assorted herbal teas
- Balsamic vinegar
- Dry beans
- Lentils
- Blue and yellow taco shells
- Blue corn chips
- Brown rice pasta
- Brown rice, quinoa, millet, corn meal, buckwheat
- Cider vinegar
- Coconut oil-optional
- Mustard
- Olive oil
- Vinegar

- Sparkling water
- Spring water
- Sesame seed oil
- Stevia
- San-J® Organic, Tamari soy sauce
- Wheat free-sugar free cereals.

OPTIONAL: **SWEETS**
- *Raw honey*
- *Agave nectar-optional*
- *Pure maple syrup*

SPROUTING
For example, mung bean sprouts, alfalfa sprouts, broccoli sprouts—Sprouting seeds at home is a great way to entice your kids to learn about growing healthy foods. An additional benefit is that they will take pride in growing them and then may be interested in trying them. Buy a sprouting container or use a glass jar. Rinse the seeds twice a day with water. In 2-3 days you will have sprouts growing in your own home. It is fun and easy.

Cooking Grains

TABLE 8.1

GRAIN	COOKING WATER	COOKING TIME	YIELD
BASMATI RICE, BROWN	2 cups	30-40 minutes	4 cups
BROWN RICE	2 cups	45-50 minutes	4 cups
CORNMEAL	4 cups	25 minutes	4 cups
MILLET	2 cups	40 minutes	3½ cups
QUINOA (Case of 24, 16 oz each)	2 cups	20-25 minutes	3½ cups

HELPFUL HINTS ON PREPARING GRAINS

① **Rinse**
Before you cook your grains, rinse them in cold water until the water runs clear. Strain them to remove any dirt or debris that might be on the grain

② **Optional Presoaking**
You can shorten cooking time by soaking grains over night. Recommended soaking time is 6-8 hours.

③ **General Rule for Cooking Grains**
2 parts water to 1 part grain.

④ **Boil/Simmer**
Bring water to a boil; add grains and return to boil. Then reduce heat and simmer. Cover tightly.

⑤ **Test**
Grains are done when they are chewy.

The chart above summarizes all that you need to know about the preparation, cooking times and yields for various grains recommended by the nutritional balancing program.

HELPFUL HINTS FOR PREPARING BEANS

① When preparing dried beans such as pinto beans, kidney beans or garbanzo beans, look for beans that are smooth and brightly colored.

② **Storing Method**
Always store in an airtight glass jar. Use within 6 months.

③ Cooked beans can be frozen up to 6 months.

④ **Preparation**
Rinse and clean beans until all debris are gone. Soak the beans. (This aids in digestion.) Cover beans completely with water. Soak beans for at least 8 hours. Then, place beans in a large pot of water and simmer beans slowly until they are tender. This makes them easier to digest.

COOKWARE

- Glass cookware is the least toxic material in which to prepare your food each day.

- Stainless steel, corningware, enamel coated, non-lead glazed ceramic cookware are also fine.

- Crock-pots are easy to use, require little prep work and provide a nutritious and delicious meal all by itself at the end of your busy day.

- Electric steamers are a wonderful addition to your kitchen tools. The advantage of the electric steamer is that you can steam several items at the same time without using other cookware. Clean up is simple with an electric steamer. It is also great for heating up leftovers. Simply place glass dishes in the steamer basket. This appliance can cut preparation time. It is a fabulous kitchen appliance.

- You can also purchase a simple vegetable steamer that fits inside a saucepan. You can steam vegetables by just putting a small amount of water in a covered saucepan and adding your vegetables. SUGGESTION: You might want to try drinking the cooking water in this case, as it will contain many minerals. You can also use a rice cooker to cook your vegetables.

- I would recommend purchasing excellent knives. It can make cutting vegetables much easier and actually pleasurable.

- Magic Bullet™ is a small mini blender and/or food processor. Easy to clean up and easy to use. A mini food processor is helpful to have on hand so that you can make soups, stews and chop vegetables.

- Nut, seed and coffee grinder

- Juicers are suggested as a means to juice your carrots and greens each day.

- Pressure cooker

- Toaster ovens are excellent for warming food quickly.

- Convection ovens are a great way to cook quickly.

- Infrared toaster oven

- Timer

- Measuring cups and spoons

A WORD ABOUT MICROWAVES

Nutritional balancing does not recommend microwaves. Microwaves can damage the cell walls of food and possibly cause an inflammatory immune response in the body. In addition, they change the texture and taste of many foods. When you take the time and spend the money for the best ingredients, it makes sense to get the best out of every ingredient you use. Don't "steam" your vegetables in the microwave. Steam them on your stovetop or use a free-standing electric steamer. Even the best poultry will lose its appeal when cooked it in a microwave. The aromas and textures of your foods are star features of your meals.

RECIPES

BREAKFAST

EGGS

GRAINS

LUNCH & DINNER

SALADS & SIDES

POULTRY

FISH

LAMB

*what makes
a recipe simple?*

Within this book there are simple recipes, easy recipes for you to whip up with little prep time, few ingredients, minimal clean-up, and of course—great taste.

If you find yourself in a panic about what to make for a meal, crunched for time or just plain tired, have no fear—just look for the symbol signifying you have found one of my simple recipes.

BOLD HIGHLIGHTS TO THE
LEFT SIGNIFY THAT THESE ARE
SIMPLE RECIPES

RECIPES FOR CHILDREN, ENJOYED BY EVERYONE

BREAKFAST

EGGS

GRAINS

LUNCH/DINNER

POULTRY

GRASS-FED BEEF

LAMB

VEGETABLES

breakfast

Good morning sunshine. Gently slide back your blankets and welcome the glorious day. As the light streams through your windows, the key question is " What's for breakfast?" Our most important meal, breakfast is necessary as your blood sugar is low after a night of sleep. Most people have not eaten for 8-10 hours. Since your body has been basically running on empty, this meal is your chance to fuel your body.

Skipping breakfast keeps your body in 'starvation' mode, while eating a good meal will give your metabolism a boost. Breakfast also provides a significant proportion of the day's total nutrient intake and offers the opportunity to eat foods filled with essential vitamins and minerals that can only be gained from food.

So what's cooking? On a weekday morning, if you are in a hurry, try some Easy Egg Drop Soup or Simply Soft Boiled Eggs. On the weekends, when you have more time, explore the many options available—Delightful Oatmeal Pancakes, Corny Tortilla French Toast–Oui Oui or even the spooky Halloween Pumpkin Pancakes.

Surprise yourself. Take some time to experiment with new flavors, tastes and textures of the food. Mix it up. Instead of having your typical fare, welcome a new aroma, a new sampling. Delight your senses with the simplicity of clean, whole food.

Make food simple and let things taste of what they are.

Maurice Edmond Sailland, French writer (1872-1956)

eggs

(simple) # Mexican Scrambled Eggs

Serves 1-2

2-4 EGGS

1 PAT OF BUTTER

1 SMALL HANDFUL OF ALFALFA SPROUTS

1 TEASPOON OF FRESH CILANTRO

8-10 BLUE CORN CHIPS

Melt butter in a small-size pan. Scramble eggs in a bowl. Pour eggs into a hot, buttered pan and stir gently over low-medium heat. When eggs are done remove from pan. Sprinkle with some fresh cilantro. Place the eggs on a plate and garnish with alfalfa sprouts and a handful of blue corn chips.

VARIATION:
You can also place this egg dish in a corn tortilla.

(simple) # Perfectly Poached Eggs in a Nest

Serves 1-2

3-4 EGGS

PINCH OF SEA SALT

2 SLICES OF RICE BREAD

1 TABLESPOON OF BUTTER

A poached egg is cooked in gently boiling water so that the yolk is runny and loose. Fill a shallow pan with water. Bring the water to a gentle boil and break the eggs into the shallow pan of water. Add in a pinch of sea salt. Cook for about 3 minutes, turn down the heat and cover the pan for about 3-5 more minutes. Use a slotted spoon to remove the eggs. Place your rice bread on a plate and cut a small circle into the center of the bread. Gently place the eggs in the hole, your nest. Enjoy.

VEGETABLES THAT CAN BE USED FOR INGREDIENTS IN EGGY VEGGIE STIR-FRY

ROOT VEGETABLES
Beets
Carrots
Celery root
Parsnip
Radishes
Rutabaga
Sweet potatoes
Turnips

BRASSICAS &
GREEN LEAFY VEGETABLES
Broccoli
Brussel sprouts
Cabbage
Cauliflower
Collard greens
Spinach
Swiss chard

PODS AND SEEDS
Corn
Green beans
Peas

PUMPKINS & SQUASHES
Acorn
Butternut
Pumpkin
Squash
Summer squashes
Winter squashes
Zucchini
Shoot vegetables
Artichokes
Asparagus
Celery
Endive
Fennel

ONION FAMILY
Garlic
Leeks
Onions

MUSHROOM FAMILY
Button
Enoki
Portabello

Eggy Veggie Stir-Fry

Serves 1-2

¼ CUP ONIONS

¼ CUP CARROTS

¼ CUP BEAN SPROUTS

2-4 EGGS

2 TABLESPOONS OLIVE OIL

Pour 2 tablespoons of olive oil into a wok/pan and place on high heat. Place all the veggies in the wok/pan. Cook vegetables for about 3-5 minutes or until done. Scramble the eggs in a bowl and then pour egg mixture in the wok/pan over the vegetables. Stir until the eggs are done. Transfer to a plate and garnish with quinoa. *(See page 183 for Quinoa recipe.)* Enjoy this healthful recipe.

 # Easy Egg Drop Soup

Serves 1

1-2 CUPS OF CHICKEN BROTH
(See page 162)

2 EGGS

Bring broth to a boil. Then scramble 2 eggs in a bowl. Pour eggs into broth, stirring constantly, until the eggs look done. This soup can be used as a light breakfast or snack.

VARIATION:
Feel free to add in frozen peas, shredded cabbage and/or chopped carrots.

CREATIVITY WITH FOOD

This dish presents many options for creativity. First, it makes great leftovers. You could easily reheat this simple meal and enjoy it for the next day. You can also rotate in a variety of vegetables to keep this dish interesting. For example, try shredded cabbage, broccoli, and turnips. Or why not try an assortment of brightly colored squash. See the list of vegetables on the next page, pick your favorites, and create your own dish.

 # Poached Eggs in a Green Nest

Variation on Poached Eggs in a Nest

Serves 1-2

3-4 EGGS

2 TABLESPOONS OF BUTTER

1 POUND OF BABY SPINACH,
WASHED AND RINSED

SEA SALT

Melt the butter in a large skillet. Sauté the spinach until it is wilted. Season with sea salt. Then begin cooking your eggs. Fill a shallow pan with water. Bring the water to a gentle boil and break the eggs into the shallow pan of water. Cook the eggs in boiling water so that the yolk is runny and loose. Add in a pinch of sea salt. Use a slotted spoon to remove the eggs. Place your cooked spinach on a plate. Make a small well in the cooked spinach and place the eggs on the spinach.

NOTE:
You can also use an egg poacher if you would like your eggs to be a little more tidy.

A WORD ON SPINACH

The nutrients found in spinach have been found to be helpful with illnesses that tend to be inflammatory—such as asthma, osteoarthritis, and rheumatoid arthritis. Additionally, this nutritional powerhouse has been shown in research to help protect the brain from free radical damage and reduce the effects of declining brain function. Researchers found that when they fed older laboratory animals diets high in spinach, that there learning capacity and motor skills improved.

Scrambled Eggs with Herbs

Serves 1-2

3-4 EGGS

¼ TEASPOON FRESH BASIL

PAT OF BUTTER

PINCH OF SEA SALT

Melt butter in a small size pan. Scramble eggs in a bowl. Pour eggs into the hot, buttered pan and add in the fresh basil. Gently stir your eggs in the pan over low-medium heat and place a pinch of sea salt in the egg mixture. Cook until done.

NOTE:
Eggs help boost brain health.

A WORD ON EGGS

According to Emory W. Thurston, PhD., author of "Nutrition for Tots to Teens", eggs are a very valuable food, providing excellent protein, minerals and vitamins. The cholesterol in these little marvels is balanced with lecithin, a compound that keeps the blood circulating and prevents deposition in the arteries.

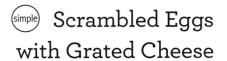 # Scrambled Eggs with Grated Cheese

Serves 1

2-3 EGGS

2 TABLESPOONS OF PARMESAN CHEESE, GRATED

PAT OF BUTTER

PINCH OF SEA SALT

Melt butter in a small size pan. Scramble eggs in a bowl. Pour eggs into the hot, buttered pan and add in the grated Parmesan cheese. Gently stir your eggs in the pan over low-medium heat. Place a pinch of sea salt in the egg mixture. Cook until done.

Scrambled Eggs with Cheesy Onions

Serves 1-2

3-4 EGGS

¼ CUP OF CHOPPED ONIONS

¼ CUP OF PARMESAN CHEESE

PAT OF BUTTER

PINCH OF SEA SALT

Melt butter in a small size pan. Sauté onions for about 5 minutes. Scramble eggs in a bowl. Then, pour eggs into the hot, buttered pan and add in the grated Parmesan cheese. Gently stir your eggs, cheese and onions in the pan over low-medium heat. Place a pinch of sea salt in the egg mixture. Cook until done.

MYTH
To avoid heart disease, use margarine instead of butter.

TRUTH
Margarine eaters have twice the rate of heart disease as butter eaters. (Nutrition Week 3/22/91 21:12)

 # Simply Soft Boiled Eggs

Serves 2

3-4 EGGS

SEA SALT

These eggs have soft egg whites and runny, loose yolks. Fill a pan with just enough water to cover the eggs. Heat to a gentle boil. Use a needle to pierce the egg shell. This will help the egg stay whole and not crack open due to pressure when cooking. Carefully place the eggs in the boiling water. Cook for about 3 minutes. Open egg and use a pinch of sea salt. Enjoy!

grains

Brown Rice Belly Warmer

Serves 2

2 EGGS

2 CUPS COOKED BROWN RICE

2 CUPS RICE MILK OR WHOLE MILK

SPRINKLE WITH A FEW BERRIES

A GOOD SIZED PINCH OF CINNAMON

¼ TEASPOON OF STEVIA OR
1 TEASPOON OF HONEY

½ TEASPOON REAL VANILLA

1 TABLESPOON BUTTER

Combine the cooked brown rice, milk, berries, cinnamon and stevia in a small pot for about 2 minutes. Spoon out a bit of the hot mixture and stir it into the bowl with the beaten eggs, slowly adding a tablespoon at a time until you have about a ⅓ cup (to prevent curdling). Stir the egg/rice mixture back into the remaining rice in the saucepan along with the vanilla and butter and continue cooking over low heat to thicken.

NOTE:
Dietary Abuses that Destroy Nutrients in the Body: *overeating, hurried eating without proper chewing, the use of caffeine, nicotine, and eating refined food or foods with chemical additives.*

Delightful Oatmeal Pancakes

Serves 2

½ CUP OLD FASHIONED OATMEAL

¼ CUP COTTAGE CHEESE

4 EGGS

1 TEASPOON OF PURE VANILLA

¼ TEASPOON CINNAMON

¼ TEASPOON NUTMEG

Process the oatmeal, cottage cheese, eggs, vanilla, cinnamon and nutmeg in a blender. Butter a skillet and pour on batter by ladleful. Cook until both sides are browned.

lunch & dinner

How often have you stood in front of the refrigerator, staring blindly at the cauliflower and ground chicken, thinking "what should I prepare?" Often, we forget how easy it is to prepare a simple meal, like taco's, because we imagine the fuss they might involve.

It is time to reroute your thinking. Instead of imagining the difficulty of the preparation, the meals provided in this section involve simple preparation and few ingredients.

This section provides a solution to the what to cook dilemma for lunch and dinner, an issue that plagues many of us. At your fingertips, you will find various lunch and dinner options that will keep you nourished, healthy and energized.

PRINCIPLES OF MEAL PLANNING

Try to keep your meals simple and uncomplicated, balancing flavors, qualities and nutritional aspects.

FOOD COMBINING

To simplify a very complicated subject regarding which foods should be eaten together and which combinations should be avoided to maximize nutrition and minimize indigestion, follow these general guidelines:

① *Fruits are best eaten alone.*
② *Vegetables and proteins combine well.*
③ *Grains and vegetables combine well.*

PREPARING FOOD AHEAD

Most of the recipes provided in this book can easily be prepared in advance. You can also freeze them, and defrost them during a busy week.

salads & sides

Greek Island Vegetable Salad

Serves 2-4

½ CUP APPLE CIDER VINEGAR

2 TABLESPOONS FLAX OIL OR HEMP OIL

2 TABLESPOONS OREGANO LEAVES
FRESHLY CHOPPED,
OR 2 TEASPOONS DRIED

½ TEASPOON SALT

2 CLOVES GARLIC, FINELY CHOPPED

1 MEDIUM CUCUMBER, SLICED

1 MEDIUM CARROT, SLICED

1 MEDIUM ONION, SLICED

6 OUNCES FRESH SPINACH LEAVES,
WASHED *(about 1 cup)*

½ CUP FETA CHEESE, CRUMBLED

In small bowl, mix vinegar, oil, oregano, sea salt, mustard, and add garlic. In a separate glass or plastic container, add in the vegetables. Pour vinegar mixture over vegetables. Cover and refrigerate for at least 1 hour to blend flavors. Place spinach on a serving platter. Top spinach with the vegetables. Sprinkle with cheese.

WHAT'S YOUR VIBE?
The right attitude is just as important as the quality of food and cooking techniques. It is believed that food prepared in anger, imparts anger. Additionally, the appearance, taste, balance, and presentation of food, and how people feel after, are said to be the counterpart of the cook's physical, mental, emotional and spiritual state.

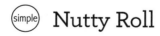 Nutty Roll

Serves 6

1 GOAT CHEESE LOG

¼ CUP OF WALNUTS, CRUSHED

RAW HONEY

CINNAMON

With a pastry brush, spread a dab of honey on the entire roll of goat cheese. Roll the goat cheese log into the crushed walnuts. Then slice the goat cheese roll into ½ inch slices. As an alternative, you can roll the goat cheese slices into some fresh cinnamon. Enjoy it! You can use as a snack, appetizer or dessert.

Sweeties-Sweet Potato Pancakes

Serves 4

4 EGGS, BEATEN

⅓ CUP RICE FLOUR

1 TEASPOON SALT

2 CUPS OF SWEET POTATO, GRATED

2 TABLESPOONS OF ONION, GRATED

DASH OF NUTMEG

¼ CUP OF BUTTER

Combine all ingredients and mix well. Form into disc shapes.

In a heavy skillet melt butter. Use a spoon to drop the mixture into the skillet. Flip to brown on both sides. Garnish with carrots. Feel free to add lots of fresh vegetables as a side.

NOTE:
Children love this recipe!!

Very Veggie Leek, Zucchini and Cheese Frittata

Serves 6

2 TABLESPOONS OLIVE OIL

3 LEEKS, THINLY SLICED

2 MEDIUM ZUCCHINIS, THINLY SLICED

1 CLOVE GARLIC, CRUSHED

SEA SALT

5 EGGS, LIGHTLY BEATEN

4 TABLESPOONS PARMESAN CHEESE, FRESHLY GRATED

4 TABLESPOONS SWISS CHEESE, CUT INTO SMALL CUBES

Heat 1 tablespoon of olive oil in small pan; add the leeks and cook, stirring over low heat until slightly softened. Cover and cook the leeks for 10 minutes. Transfer to a bowl and allow to cool. Then add sea salt, eggs and cheeses. Heat the remaining oil in the pan; add egg mixture. Cook over low heat for 15 minutes or until the frittata is almost set. Bake in oven, at 350°F for about 5 minutes or until the top is set and golden. Allow the frittata to stand for 5 minutes before cutting into wedges for serving. Place a fresh green salad on the side for lunch or as a light snack.

(simple) Oh My, Megan's Outrageous Steamed Vegetable Salad

Serves 2-4

BEETS

RUTABAGAS

BROCCOLI

GOAT CHEESE, CRUMBLED

GREEK DRESSING:

2 CUPS OF OLIVE OIL

½ CUP OF ORGANIC APPLE CIDER VINEGAR

1 TABLESPOON OF GARLIC POWDER OR 3 CLOVES OF FRESH GARLIC, MINCED

1 TABLESPOON OF SEA SALT

½ TABLESPOON OF OREGANO

Place the vegetables in a steamer basket and cook until done. Peel off the skins of the beets and rutabagas when cool. Cut up the broccoli, beets and rutabagas into small bite sizes pieces. Set aside. Prepare the salad dressing by mixing together the olive oil and vinegar and then adding in the garlic, sea salt and oregano. Pour the dressing over the vegetables and add some crumbled goat cheese. Enjoy!

VARIATION:
This dish can be enjoyed by steaming up additional varieties of vegetables to make your own warm salad combinations. You can even try other types of dressings—perhaps tahini or even different grated cheeses. Be creative and craft your own special salad.

(simple) Broiled One Dish Chicken

Serves 1

⅓ POUND OF CHICKEN THIGHS
OR BREASTS

2 TABLESPOONS OF SOFTENED BUTTER

1 CARROT, SLICED

1 PARSNIP, SLICED

SEA SALT

Preheat oven to 400° F. Mix lemon juice and sea salt and then baste the chicken breast or thigh. Dot the chicken with butter. Place chicken in a buttered dish with the sliced carrots and parsnip. Broil for 15 minutes a side.

VARIATION:
Chicken thighs are tastier and healthier than chicken breasts because they contain healthy fat. You could make a simple dish, by placing the chicken thighs in a steamer for about 20 minutes or in the oven for about 30 minutes.

Chopped Chicken Salad

Serves 4

1 POUND OF CHICKEN BREASTS,
CUT INTO CHUNKS

2-3 TABLESPOONS OF HEALTHY
MAYONNAISE *(No high fructose corn syrup)*

½ CUP OF WALNUTS, CHOPPED

1 CUP OF CELERY, CHOPPED

Bake the chicken breasts at 350°F for approximately 20 minutes. When done, remove from oven and let cool. Add in mayonnaise, celery and walnuts. Mix together.

(simple) Carousel Turkey Surprise

Serves 2-4

8 RYE CRACKERS

4 TEASPOONS OF DIJON MUSTARD

8 SLICES OF ORGANIC, OR RAW CHEESE

EIGHT, 1 OUNCE TURKEY SLICES

¼ CUP BROCCOLI SPROUTS

Spread each rye cracker with ½ teaspoon of mustard. Place one slice of cheese and turkey on each cracker. Top with a table-spoon of sprouts.

VARIATION:
If you would like to skip the cracker, you could use lettuce leafs.

NOTE:
Purchase rye crackers that have no added sugar, chemical additives or sweeteners.

MUSTARD
This popular spice is part of the cabbage family. It is an excellent source of Omega-3 fatty acids, calcium, iron, manganese, magnesium, niacin, phosphorus, protein, selenium, and zinc. To name just a few benefits this spice improves your health by: speeding up your metabolism, stimulating digestion, inhibiting cancer cell growth and reducing the severity of asthma.

A house is not a home unless it contains food and fire for the mind as well as the body.

Benjamin Franklin

Chicken and Cauliflower with Infused Indian Flavors

Serves 4

4 CHICKEN THIGHS

4 TABLESPOONS OF BUTTER

2 CUPS OF CAULIFLOWER

½ TEASPOON OF RED CURRY POWDER

1 TEASPOON OF TURMERIC

SEA SALT

Sprinkle chicken with red curry powder. Then season with sea salt. Heat up a large skillet with 3 tablespoons of butter. Place the chicken in the pan and brown both sides. Cook each side for about 10 minutes or until cooked through. When done, remove from pan. In a new pan, add in the remaining 1 tablespoon of butter and the turmeric and let it cook for 1-2 minutes before placing the cauliflower in the skillet. Once the cauliflower is added, cook for an additional 5 minutes and remove from pan. Enjoy this dish.

NOTE:
This ancient spice, turmeric, is a must have for every spice cabinet.

DID YOU KNOW?

Turmeric gets it name from the Sanskrit word for yellow. This spice has been known to fight arthritis, cancer and inflammation. You can find turmeric easily in your spice aisle at the market. Please note that like all spices, it loses its flavor after a 6-month period.

FUN FACT

In India, Band-Aids are saturated with turmeric. The ability of turmeric to heal wounds is well established in India. You might want to try this remedy on a minor cut by making a paste of turmeric and water. You can apply this to the area for about one hour.

Chicken Stir Fry

Serves 4

1 POUND OF CHICKEN BREASTS,
CUT INTO SMALL PIECES

1 TEASPOON OF FRESH GARLIC

1 TEASPOON OF GINGER

½ CUP OF ONIONS

½ CUP OF BROCCOLI

4 TABLESPOONS OF DARK SESAME OIL

1 TEASPOON OF SAN-J® ORGANIC,
GLUTEN-FREE TAMARI SOY SAUCE

STIR-FRYING

Stir-frying is an Asian technique that is a quick and easy way to cook meat and vegetables. An added bonus is that the food retains its texture and flavor. Stir-frying involves a quick sauté over high heat. So, if you do not have lots of time, this dish is the answer for you.

You can stir-fry in any skillet! Cut all your veggies first as this dish cooks quickly.

Put your skillet on the cook top and turn up the heat to high. Then, pour in 2 teaspoons of sesame oil into the wok or skillet. Place the chicken in the pan and stir-fry until well browned and cooked through. This should take about 2 to 3 minutes. Take the chicken out of the pan and place on plate. Then add in the remaining oil, garlic and onions. Let that cook for about 2 minutes. Add in remaining vegetables and cook for 3 minutes. Remove the vegetables and place on plate with chicken. Place tamari on the chicken and vegetables when food is plated.

NOTE:
Quick and easy ideas for marinades on your meats and vegetables—mix olive oil and fresh herbs. Try using parsley, chives and basil. You can also add in some lemon juice and sea salt. Another easy option is to mix in toasted sesame oil, soy sauce, rice vinegar, and garlic.

ALSO:
Arrowroot or cornstarch make nice thickening agents for sauces.

VARIATION:
Try using coconut oil to add a different flavor to this easy dish.

To make this dish even simpler—buy pre-shredded vegetables such as:

* *Shredded carrots*
* *Broccoli-coleslaw mix*
* *Sliced mushrooms*
* *Snow peas*

You can add these easy veggies in to the stir-fry as well or save these ingredients for another time.

 Deli Roll Ups

Serves 1

2-4 SLICES OF NATURAL OR
FRESH TURKEY BREAST

2 ROMAINE LETTUCE LEAVES

1 HANDFUL OF SPROUTS

1 ONION, SLICED

2 TEASPOONS CARROTS, SHREDDED

1 TEASPOON OF MUSTARD

1 TEASPOON OF MAYONNAISE

Place your lettuce leaves on a plate. Using a butter knife spread the mayonnaise and mustard on the lettuce leaves. Carefully craft your roll up by placing a layer of turkey slices, sprouts, onions and carrots. When you have completed designing your meal, roll up your lettuce with all of the delicious ingredients and enjoy.

Finger Licking Chicken Cutlets

Serves 6

1½ POUNDS OF CHICKEN CUTLETS

2 TEASPOONS OF SEA SALT

2 TABLESPOONS OLIVE OIL

4 SCALLIONS, SLICED

2 TABLESPOONS OF FRESH
TARRAGON LEAVES, CHOPPED

Season each chicken cutlet with ½ teaspoon salt. Heat the oil in a large skillet over medium high heat. Working in 2 batches, cook the chicken until browned and cooked through. This should take about 2-3 minutes per side. Plate the chicken. Top with scallions and tarragon.

(simple) Great Grandma's Turkey Patties with Zucchini & Onions

Serves 4

1 POUND NATURAL OR ORGANIC
DARK TURKEY, GROUND

1 CUP OF ZUCCHINI, GRATED

1 CUP OF ONIONS, MINCED

In a medium size bowl, mix the ground turkey, zucchini, and onion together. Form the turkey mixture into patties and place either on the grill or in the broiler. Cook on the grill for 6 minutes per side. Cook in the broiler for about 6-8 minutes per side, or until done.

VARIATION:
You can also make "green burgers" by shredding up some spinach and mixing it together with the ground turkey.

MYTH
Vegetarianism is healthy.

TRUTH
The annual all-cause death rate of vegetarian men is slightly more than that of non-vegetarian men (.93 percent vs .89 percent); the annual death rate of vegetarian women is significantly more than that of non-vegetarian women (.86 percent vs .54 percent) (Am J Clin Nutr 1982 36:873)

For perfect health, food should always be eaten as fresh as possible both after plucking as well as after cooking. The more it is kept, the more it will loose it's vital quality and the less likely it is to produce vitality in us.

Banamali, Nitya Yoga: Essays on the Sreemad Bhagavad Gita

One Dish Dinner: Succulent Roasted Chicken

Serves 4

1 WHOLE NATURAL ROASTING CHICKEN

1 MEDIUM ONION, SLICED

3 LARGE CARROTS, SLICED

1 LARGE HEAD OF ELEPHANT GARLIC

3 TABLESPOONS OLIVE OIL

COARSE SEA SALT

PAPRIKA

2 CUPS OF WATER

Wash off the chicken and pat dry. Place chicken in a large roasting pan. Season the chicken with the oil, paprika, and salt. Inside the chicken place a clove of whole garlic and a whole onion. Surround the chicken with the remaining sliced vegetables. Add about 2 cups of water into the base of the pan to keep the chicken moist. Bake in oven at 350°F for approximately 1½-2 hours. Slice up and enjoy!

VARIATION:
Try substituting different root vegetables. For example, you can exchange parsnips for carrots or rutabagas.

Quick and Easy Crisp Southwestern Salad

Serves 4

2 SMALL HEADS OF LEAF LETTUCE

ONE, 15 OUNCE CAN PINTO BEANS, DRAINED AND RINSED

2 EARS CORN, KERNELS OFF THE COB

½ RED ONION, THINLY SLICED

½ CUP FRESH CILANTRO SPRIGS

9 OUNCE BAG OF BLUE CORN CHIPS

12 OUNCES OF NATURAL OR FRESH TURKEY BREAST

SALAD DRESSING:

¼ CUP OF FLAX OIL OR HEMP OIL

¼ CUP FRESH LIME JUICE

¼ TEASPOON GROUND CUMIN

In a large bowl, combine the lettuce, beans, corn, onion and cilantro. Cut up slices of turkey and place on the salad. To prepare the salad dressing, mix together the flax seed oil, lime juice and ground cumin. Add blue corn chips as a garnish or you could place them around the inside of the bowl. Quick and easy!

NOTE:
Are you feeling blue? Blue corn chips have health benefits. They have more protein, and less starch than other chips. They also are high in antioxidants.

(simple) Tossed Garbage Salad

Serves 4 or more

HARD-BOILED EGGS

CHICKPEAS

SUNFLOWER SEEDS

RAW MILK PARMESAN CHEESE, SLICED

LEAFY LETTUCE

STEAMED CAULIFLOWER

STEAMED BROCCOLI

CHICKEN, SLICED

Chop all the ingredients into bite size portions. Choose the amount of each ingredient you would like in the salad. Serve with the dressing you love!

NOTE:
Romaine and dark leaf lettuce are more nutritious than iceberg lettuce.

> **THE ART OF CHEWING**
> *Enjoy the aromas and tastes that create your meal. Simply chew and be grateful for your delectable meal. Carbohydrate digestions begins in the mouth and this process of chewing changes grains and other complex carbohydrates into sugars and makes oil, proteins and minerals available for absorption. Your body will thank you!*

(simple) Turkey Plus Parmesan Salad

Serves 2

1 LARGE HEAD GREEN LEAF LETTUCE

½ POUND OF NATURAL OR FRESH SLICED TURKEY

½ CUP RED ONION

½ CUP SHAVED PARMESAN CHEESE

SALAD DRESSING:

4 TABLESPOONS FLAX SEED OIL OR HEMP OIL

2 TABLESPOONS BALSAMIC VINEGAR

Arrange salad in a bowl. Garnish with turkey, onions and shaved Parmesan cheese. In a separate bowl, mix the dressing: flax seed/hemp oil and vinegar together. Pour over salad when ready to serve. Enjoy!

NOTE:
Hemp and flax oils are high in Omega-3's.

 _fish_

(simple) Baked Salmon Surprise

Serves 4

1 POUND OF SALMON FILET

2 TABLESPOONS OF BUTTER, SOFTENED

1 TABLESPOON OF DILL

DASH OF SEA SALT

Rinse off the fish and pat dry. Use butter to grease the bottom of the large baking dish. Place fish in pan. Sprinkle dill, softened butter and salt over the filet. Bake at 325°F for about fifteen minutes or until tender.

THIS IS FISHY

Recent news headlines herald new biotech GMO Salmon. The AquAdvantage salmon, developed by Aqua Bounty Technologies Inc, are genetically modified to grow twice as fast as conventional Atlantic salmon. Environmental and food-safety critics plan to fight against approval. Additionally, reports state that this could lead the way for biotech trout and tilapia. Be careful to inquire where your salmon is being purchased from so that you know whether your salmon is a GMO fish.

(simple) Broiled Salmon

Serves 2

1-2 SALMON FILETS ABOUT 4-6 OUNCES EACH

2 CLOVES OF GARLIC

2 TEASPOONS DILL

2 TABLESPOONS OLIVE OIL

SEA SALT

Preheat oven to broil. Place fish on an oiled baking tray. Brush olive oil on to the fish. Mince the garlic through a garlic press and spread on fish. Then add dill and sea salt. Cook for 10-15 minutes. Easy!

NOTE:
Salmon is high in protein and essential fatty acids, called Omega-3's.

Simply Splendid Salmon

Serves 2

1 POUND OF SALMON, SKIN OFF

EXTRA VIRGIN OLIVE OIL

LEMON, THINLY SLICED

SAN-J® ORGANIC, GLUTEN-FREE
TAMARI SOY SAUCE

ORGANIC TARRAGON FLAKES

Coat both grill and fish lightly with extra virgin olive oil. Then cut fish in half for ease of handling. Make 4-6 cuts along the fat lines in each piece and insert thin slivers of lemon. Use 2 light shakes of soy sauce for each half. Finish with tarragon flakes to taste. Marinate in the refrigerator for an hour. Broil on high. Cook for about 20-30 minutes

Easy Roll Ups Smoked Salmon and Goat Cheese

Serves 1-2

2-4 SLICES SMOKED SALMON

2-4 SLICES OF GOAT CHEESE

A FEW SLICES OF RED ONION

ALFALFA SPROUTS

Lay out the smoked salmon on a plate. Place the goat cheese, onion, and sprouts on top of the smoked salmon. Roll up the salmon with the ingredients inside. This is a nice snack or lunch. Add some freshly steamed vegetables, as a side, to enjoy this easy meal.

From Down Under the Sea... Nori Roll Up

Serves 2 or more

2 CUPS OF COOKED BROWN RICE

2 SHEETS OF NORI

1 CAN OF SARDINES OR SMOKED SALMON

1 CUP OF CARROTS, SHREDDED

SAN-J® ORGANIC, GLUTEN-FREE
TAMARI SOY SAUCE

Slice sardines or salmon and carrots. Lay a sheet of nori shiny side down. Spread 1 cup of cooked brown rice on 1 sheet of Nori. Then place salmon or sardines and carrots in the middle of the rice. Roll carefully and then slice with a dampened knife. Dip the wrap in tamari.

NOTE:
Nori, an edible seaweed, is available in the Asian section of the market. This sea vegetable is an excellent source of iodine, fiber, protein, vitamin C, iron and zinc. Iodine is used by every cell in the body.

Fishing for a Compliment: Sarah's Sardine Tart

Serves 6

1 UNBAKED GLUTEN FREE PIE SHELL

2 LARGE ONIONS, CHOPPED

2 LARGE ZUCCHINIS, CHOPPED

2 TABLESPOONS OLIVE OIL

2 TEASPOONS DRIED THYME

SEA SALT TO TASTE

TWO, 5 OUNCE CANS SARDINES, PACKED IN OLIVE OIL

Cook the onions in olive oil on medium heat for 10 minutes. Season with thyme and sea salt. Spread the onions and zucchini in the gluten free pie shell and bake at 400°F for 20 minutes. Remove the sardines from their cans and break them into bits (it's fine to leave the bones in the sardines). Remove the tart from the oven, spread the sardine bits evenly across the surface and bake for five minutes longer. Serve hot or warm.

 ## This is Fishy: Sardines and Chopped Eggs

Serves 4

1 FLAT CAN SARDINES IN MUSTARD

2 FLAT CANS SARDINES IN OIL

4 HARD-BOILED EGGS

FRESH PARSLEY

Place sardines in mustard in a small bowl; then mash. Place the mashed sardines on a large plate. Drain the remaining sardines in oil; then place remaining sardines on a large plate. (Make sure there are two places for the sardines on the same large plate—one for the mashed sardines in mustard and one for the sardines placed into a shape like a fan) Place 4 eggs in boiling water until they are hard boiled. Chop the eggs until they are finely diced. Spread the chopped eggs around the two types of sardines, and garnish with parsley. Place border of parsley around sardines.

(simple) Sardines in the Pan with Garlic

Serves 4

8 SARDINES

2 TABLESPOONS OF OLIVE OIL

2 CLOVES OF GARLIC

SEA SALT

Heat the oil in a skillet. Cook the cloves of garlic until fragrant and soft. Add sardines and cook for 4-5 minutes. Place the sardines and garlic on a plate with a pinch of sea salt.

(simple) Sardines on the Grill

Serves 2

12 SARDINES

1-2 TABLESPOONS OF LEMON JUICE

1 TABLESPOON OF BUTTER

6 LEAVES OF ROMAINE LETTUCE

Drain all the liquid from the sardines. Turn on the grill to medium heat. Place sardines in a grill basket. Melt the butter and add in lemon juice. Pour over the sardines. Cook on grill for about 5 minutes. Line up the romaine lettuce on a plate and place two sardines on each leaf of lettuce. Roll up and enjoy!

A WORD ON SARDINES

These nutritional powerhouses are one of the best sources of Omega-3 fats, with a whopping 1,950 mg/per 3 oz. (that's more per serving than salmon, tuna or just about any other food) and they're packed with Vitamin D.

(simple) Broiled Lamb Chops

Serves 4

4 LAMB CHOPS

SEA SALT

Preheat the broiler. Season the lamb with a pinch of sea salt and place meat in oven.

Broil the lamb chops for about 5 minutes per side. Bon Appetite!

(simple) Grilled and Glazed Lamb Burgers

Serves 4

1 ¼ POUNDS GROUND LAMB

SEA SALT

¼ CUP OF TERIYAKI SAUCE

3 KIRBY CUCUMBERS CUT INTO SPEARS

Heat grill to medium high. Form the ground lamb into 4-half-inch thick patties and season with ½ teaspoon sea salt. Grill burgers for 4-5 minutes for side for medium, basting with the teriyaki sauce during the last 2 minutes of cooking. Serve with cucumbers on the side.

(simple) Lamb and Minced Onions

Serves 1

¼ POUND OF LAMB, GROUND

½ SMALL ONION, MINCED

1 TABLESPOON OF OLIVE OIL

Fire up your grill or turn on your oven to broil. In a small pan, add in 1 tablespoon of olive oil. Then add onions. Sauté for about 5 minutes. When the onions are soft, add them to the ground lamb. Shape meat into a patty. Place on a hot grill for 5-6 minutes per side for medium rare. You can also place your patties in the oven on broil for the same time. Make it easy! Enjoy.

NOTE:
Lamb is an excellent source of protein. Always purchase grass-fed meats.

Leg of Lamb

Serves 4

4-POUND LEG OF LAMB WITH BONE IN

OLIVE OIL

SEA SALT

½ TEASPOON OF ROSEMARY

Preheat oven to 350°F. Place the lamb, in a shallow roasting pan with the fat side facing up. Baste with oil, sea salt and rosemary. Roast for about 1 and ½ hours. Let rest for about 5 minutes and slice.

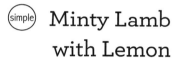 Minty Lamb with Lemon

Serves 4

4 LAMB STEAKS
(cut from top of back leg-boneless)

1 CLOVE GARLIC, CRUSHED

2 TEASPOONS MINT

2 TABLESPOONS OF OLIVE OIL

SEA SALT

JUICE FROM ONE LEMON

Make a marinade for the lamb by mixing garlic, mint, olive oil, lemon juice and sea salt. Place meat in the marinade in shallow dish. Best if the meat can be refrigerated and sit overnight in this mixture, but not necessary. Broil lamb under high heat for about 7-8 minutes per side.

Everything's a test,
To see what you will do;
Mistaking what's before
your eyes, You have to
start anew!

Chinese Zen – Hsuan Hua

grass-fed beef

Succulent Steak with a Side of Mushroom Salad

Serves 4

3 TABLESPOONS FRESH BALSAMIC VINEGAR

4 TABLESPOONS OF FLAX OIL OR HEMP OIL

TWO, 8 OUNCE PACKAGES MUSHROOMS, SLICED

½ CUP FRESH PARSLEY LEAVES, CHOPPED

1¼ POUNDS NATURAL OR GRASS-FED SKIRT STEAK

SEA SALT

In a large bowl, combine the balsamic vinegar, 4 tablespoons of oil, ½ teaspoon salt. Add the mushrooms, parsley and toss to combine. Cut the steak into pieces as necessary to fit in a large skillet. Season with ½ teaspoon of oil in the skillet over medium high-heat. Cook the steak to your taste, about 6-7 minutes per side for medium rare. Slice the steak and serve with the mushroom salad.

NOTE:
Grass-fed beef is your blue ribbon winner. Always try to purchase this type of meat when it is available. If it is not available, try to purchase organic or free range meats.

Hubby Bubby's Marinated Flank Steak (Yum!)

Serves 4-6

2 TABLESPOONS OLIVE OIL

1 SMALL RED ONION

⅓ CUP BALSAMIC VINEGAR

2 TABLESPOONS FRESH OREGANO, CHOPPED

3 CLOVES GARLIC, MINCED

1 ½ POUNDS OF NATURAL OR GRASS-FED FLANK STEAK

¼ TEASPOON OF SALT

Sliver one-quarter of the onion and set aside. (This will be used for the marinade.) Chop the remaining portion of the onion. Mix the vinegar, olive oil, oregano and garlic all together. Combine ¼ cup of this mixture with the chopped onions and set aside to be sautéed later. Sprinkle both sides of the steak with the sea salt: prick well with a fork. In a large zip top food bag, combine the steak, sliced onions, with the remaining onion mixture. Marinate for 1 hour or overnight. *(I recommend overnight.)* Place the marinated meat on the heated grill. Grill for 5-6 minutes each side. Let the meat rest for 5 minutes before slicing. Place the meat on a platter and pour the reserved sautéed onion mixture over the steak.

(simple) Mouthwatering Florentine Style T- Bone

Serves 4-6

1½ POUNDS OF PRIME NATURAL OR
GRASS-FED T-BONE STEAK

⅓ CUP FRESH GARLIC, MINCED

1 CUP PARSLEY, CHOPPED

1 CUP BASIL, CHOPPED

1 CUP OF OLIVE OIL

Heat the grill. Mix the garlic, parsley, basil and olive oil together. Marinate the steak for about 1 hour. Place on the grill and cook for about 6 minutes per side for medium rare.

USING THE CROCK-POT—ALSO KNOWN AS SLOW COOKING

The Crock-pot is one of the best time saving appliances in the kitchen. It's great for those people who are busy, or lack the energy to prepare their meals. All you need to do is fill it and turn it on. Hours later, you have a home filled with wonderful smells and dinner that is ready for the table.

MORE CROCK-POT ADVANTAGES

- *Offers all day cooking and you will not have to do any looking*

- *Food does not overcook or burn*

- *Foods cooked slowly will become very tender*

- *Easy to prepare foods- simply put all ingredients into the pot*

- *Because food simmers in its own juices, it is tastier than boiled foods*

- *Economical to operate*

- *Easy clean up*

- *Cook overnight-or throughout the day without lots of supervision*

- *Low temperature that is great for retaining nutrients*

- *Can use the interior ceramic bowl to store leftovers in the refrigerator*

- *They do not heat up the kitchen*

- *They also come with simple recipe books to get started*

soups and stews

Apple of My Eye Brisket

CROCK-POT RECIPE

Cook on high for 5 hours
Makes 10-12 Servings

2½ TO 3 POUNDS FRESH GRASS-FED,
NATURAL OR ORGANIC BRISKET

8 OUNCE JAR OF APPLESAUCE

4 LARGE APPLES, CHOPPED

10 OUNCE CAN OF TOMATOES, CHOPPED

6 OUNCE CAN OF TOMATO PASTE

3 CARROTS, SLICED

1 MEDIUM SIZED ONION, CUBED

2 CLOVES OF GARLIC

1 TEASPOON OF SEA SALT

24 OUNCES OF WATER

Trim fat from meat. If necessary, cut meat to fit into 3-5 quart slow cooker. Place meat into cooker. In a bowl, place applesauce, diced apples, chopped tomatoes, tomato paste, salt and water. Stir the ingredients together. Then pour over meat. Cover and cook on a high heat setting for about 5 hours or a low heat setting for about 10 hours or until meat is tender. Remove meat, save the juices and cover to keep warm. Pour cooking juices into a saucepan and bring to a boil to reduce the broth. Boil gently and uncovered for 15-20 minutes or until reduced consistency, stirring frequently. Thinly slice the meat across the grain and drizzle with cooking juices.

The quest for slowness, which begins as a simple rebellion against the impoverishment of taste in our lives, makes it possible to rediscover taste.

Carlo Petrini, "Slow Food Nation"

Claudia's Favorite Crock-Pot Recipe

CROCK-POT RECIPE

Serves 6

TWO 1 POUND GRASS FED, NATURAL OR ORGANIC CROSS CUT STEAKS
(a cross cut steak is made by cutting across the chuck to produce steaks)

¼ CUP BALSAMIC VINEGAR

16 OUNCES OF BEEF BROTH

1 TABLESPOON OF GARLIC, CRUSHED
(if you'd like, you can add lots of garlic)

1 TURNIP

1 SMALL ONION

SEA SALT TO TASTE

Arrange the steaks on the bottom of the crock-pot. Add in all the ingredients, cutting up the turnip into bite size chunks. Cook for eight hours.

Hot and Healthy Turkey Sausage Stew

CROCK-POT RECIPE

Serves 4

1 POUND TURKEY SAUSAGE

3 SWEET POTATOES, PEELED

2 STALKS OF CELERY

½ ONION

24 OUNCES WATER

1 CAN TOMATOES, DICED

1 TABLESPOON OF GARLIC
(feel free to add more or less)

SEA SALT TO TASTE

3 TABLESPOONS EXTRA VIRGIN OLIVE OIL

Slice turkey sausage, celery and onions into bite-sized pieces. Arrange in layers in crock-pot. Add all other ingredients. Set crock-pot for 6 hours.

> **NIGHTSHADES**
> This recipe has tomatoes, members of the nightshade family that can aggravate inflammatory conditions.

(simple) Lamb Stew

CROCK-POT RECIPE

Serves 4

1 LEG OF LAMB

1 POUND BAG CARROTS,
CUT IN BITE SIZED PIECES

1 LEEK

1 LARGE RED ONION

2 MEDIUM PARSNIPS

2 CUPS GREEN BEANS

4 LARGE CLOVES OF GARLIC, MINCED

1 TEASPOON ROSEMARY

1 TEASPOON THYME

1 TEASPOON SEA SALT

2 TABLESPOONS ARROWROOT OR
CORNSTARCH

¼ CUP WATER

Cut lamb into 2 inch cubes, removing most fat. If bone is available, add it too. Cut all veggies in bite-sized pieces. Place in crock-pot. Add garlic, rosemary, thyme and sea salt. Cook on low heat for all day cooking, or high heat for 2-3 hours. Approximately 30 minutes before serving mix arrowroot with water and pour into stew for thickening. Adjust spices to taste.

(simple) Smashing Sweet Potatoes and Parsnips

CROCK-POT RECIPE

Serves 6

4 CUPS OF SWEET POTATOES, DICED

3 CUPS OF MEDIUM PARSNIPS,
PEELED AND CUBED

4 CUPS OF WATER

2 TABLESPOONS OF BUTTER, MELTED

½ TEASPOON OF SEA SALT

½ CUP OF CHOPPED APPLES

Gently oil the inside of the crock-pot. Place all the ingredients in the crock-pot. Cover and cook for 6-8 hours on the low heat setting.

(simple) Cream of Broccoli Soup

Serves 2

1 TABLESPOON UNSALTED BUTTER

¾ CUP ONION, CHOPPED

SEA SALT TO TASTE

¾ POUND BROCCOLI, CHOPPED

1 CARROT, SLICED THINLY

3 CUPS WATER

¼ CUP SOUR CREAM OR YOU CAN USE
1 CUP PLUS 4 TEASPOONS OF RAW CREAM

Melt butter in a heavy saucepan over medium heat. Add onion and sea salt. When the onion starts to soften, add broccoli and carrot and cook until vegetables are soft. Add 1 cup water and simmer for about 20 minutes. Pureé soup in batches until smooth. Now use a heavy saucepan and transfer soup then begin adding the remaining 2 cups water. Heat soup over low heat and slowly mix in sour cream or raw cream.

CREAM
It is best not to cook cream, but rather to warm it at the end of preparing this soup. This minimizes damaging the benefits of raw cream.

(simple) Teeny Weenie Split Pea & Turkey Sausage Soup

Serves 4

2 CUPS DRY YELLOW SPLIT PEAS

2 CUPS CHOPPED COOKED ALL NATURAL
TURKEY SAUSAGE

1½ CUPS CARROTS, COARSELY SHREDDED

½ CUP CHIVES, CHOPPED

1 CLOVE GARLIC

1 TABLESPOON SNIPPED FRESH BASIL

1 TABLESPOON OREGANO

5 CUPS WATER

½ CUP CANNED TOMATOES

Rinse split peas and drain. In a 4 quart slow cooker combine the split peas, turkey sausage, carrots, chives, garlic, dried basil, oregano and canned tomatoes. Pour water over all. Cover and cook on low heat setting for 6-8 hours or on high heat for 3-4 hours.

NIGHTSHADES
This recipe has tomatoes, members of the nightshade family that can aggravate inflammatory conditions.

(simple) Twisted Pumpkin Soup

Serves 4

15 OUNCE CAN OF PUMPKIN
(fresh pumpkin is best)

1 CUP CELERY, CHOPPED

½ CUP CARROT, CHOPPED

½ CUP ONION, CHOPPED

¼ TEASPOON SEA SALT

¼ TEASPOON GINGER, GROUND

28 OUNCES OF WATER

¼ CUP OF HEAVY CREAM

PUMPKIN SEEDS, TOASTED & SHELLED OR
DRY-ROASTED SUNFLOWER
SEEDS, SHELLED

In a 4-quart slow cooker place pumpkin, celery, carrots, onion, sea salt, and ginger. Stir in water. Cover and cook on low heat for 6-8 hours or on high heat for 3-4 hours. Stir in cream. Ladle into bowls. Sprinkle with seeds.

VEGETABLE PEELS
The peels of the root vegetables, although they can be bitter, contain beneficial nutrients. I recommend leaving them on your vegetables.

Autumn Vegetable Soup

Serves 4

3 MEDIUM ONIONS,
PEELED AND CHOPPED

4 CARROTS, SLICED

2 TURNIPS, SLICED

1 RUTABAGA, SLICED

4 TABLESPOONS OF BUTTER

1½ QUARTS OF WATER

1 CLOVE GARLIC

A PINCH OF SEA SALT

Melt butter in a large, stainless steel pot and add onions, carrots, turnips, and rutabaga. Cover and simmer gently for about ½ hour over low heat, stirring occasionally. Add water and bring to a boil. Add garlic and pinch of sea salt. Simmer covered, for another ½ hour, until veggies are soft. Remove, and purée soup in a blender or food processor. If soup is too thick, add extra water to thin down the consistency.

Carrot Ginger Soup

Serves 6

1 TABLESPOON OF SAFFLOWER OIL

1½ CUPS ONIONS, SLICED

1½ TABLESPOONS GINGERROOT,
PEELED AND CHOPPED

4 CUPS CARROTS, CHOPPED
(5-6 large carrots)

4 CUPS WATER

½ TEASPOON SEA SALT

½ CUP OF HEAVY CREAM

¼ CUP FRESH CHIVES, CHOPPED

In a large pot, heat the oil and sauté the onions for about 5 minutes. Add the ginger and sauté for one minute. Stir the carrots and water and bring to a boil. Add the sea salt. Reduce heat and simmer for about 40 minutes. In a blender, purée the mixture adding the cream. Return the mixture to the pot and reheat at a low temperature.

NOTE:
This is a delicious, delicately flavored soup perfect for a cold afternoon.

(simple) Creamy Zucchini Soup

Serves 4-6

1½ CUPS OF ONIONS, SLICED

6 CUPS ZUCCHINI, CHOPPED

2½ CUPS WATER

1 TEASPOON SEA SALT

1 TABLESPOON BASIL, CHOPPED

½ CUP OF HEAVY CREAM

In a large pot, layer the onions, and zucchini. Cover with water and boil. Add the sea salt, and basil. Reduce heat to a simmer, cover and cook for about 40 minutes. Then transfer mixture to a blender, adding the cream, making sure that all ingredients are combined well. Return the soup to the pot, and reheat.

In The Beginning...Start with Basic Stock....

Serves 6

3-5 POUND ROASTING CHICKEN

3 LARGE YELLOW ONIONS, UNPEELED, QUARTERED

6 CARROTS, UNPEELED, HALVED

4 CELERY STALKS WITH LEAVES, CUT IN THIRDS

4 PARSNIPS, UNPEELED, HALVED

2 SPRIGS FRESH PARSLEY

2 SPRIGS FRESH DILL

1 HEAD OF GARLIC, PEELED, CUT IN HALF

2 TABLESPOONS SEA SALT

10 CUPS WATER

Place the chicken, onions, carrot, celery, parsnips, parsley, dill, garlic and seasonings in a large stockpot. Add in water and bring to a boil. Simmer covered for about 2½ hours. Strain the entire contents of the pot through a colander. Your broth that is created is the basic recipe for chicken broth, which can be used in a variety of recipes.

NOTE:
The solids, the chicken and vegetables, which were strained through the colander for this stock can be used as a separate meal.

Joy's Chicken Soup

Serves 4

1 WHOLE CHICKEN

1-2 MEDIUM ONIONS, QUARTERED

2 STALKS CELERY, CUT IN HALF

2 CARROTS, QUARTERED

2 PARSNIPS

1 CLOVE GARLIC, MINCED

28 OUNCES OF WATER

3-4 TABLESPOONS SEA SALT

Transfer chicken to a soup pot and add onion, celery, carrots, parsnips, garlic, sea salt and add in the recommended measurements of water. Bring to a boil. Then reduce heat and simmer, covered, for 1-2 hours. Remove vegetables and chicken from pot. Slice chicken breast into bite-size pieces and return to pot. Cut up all the vegetables coarsely and return to pot.

Mix & Match Vegetable Stew

Serves 4

4 CUPS OF WATER

2 CUPS CARROTS, SLICED

4 CUPS SUMMER SQUASH,
CUT INTO CHUNKS

1 BAG OF FROZEN CORN,
THAWED, RINSED AND DRAINED
(or 2 ears fresh corn, 1½ cups)

1 TEASPOON THYME

1 CUP ONION, COARSELY CHOPPED

*(Add other favorite vegetables such as
broccoli, cauliflower, etc.)*

Heat water in a large pot and bring to a boil. Add carrots to the water and simmer for 5 minutes. Purée the squash and add it in. Add the remaining ingredients and continue cooking for 15 minutes over medium heat. Remove from flame and let it sit for 5 minutes to allow stew to thicken.

VARIATION:
Try rotating other favorite vegetables into this dish. For example, try broccoli, cauliflower, and cabbage. Create your own favorite vegetable stew.

DID YOU KNOW?
Homemade soup provides a great way to sneak healthful ingredients into your diet, while also avoiding the chemical additives that are placed in store-bought soup brands. You can easily enhance the flavors of your soup with fresh garlic, onions and healthful herbs which provide immune building benefits.

 (simple)

Quick and Easy Onion Soup

Serves 2-4

5 LARGE RED ORGANIC ONIONS,
CHOPPED IN BITE SIZE PIECES

3 TABLESPOONS OF OLIVE OIL

4 CUPS PURE WATER

1 BAY LEAF

1 TEASPOON SEA SALT

PARMESAN CHEESE (OPTIONAL)

Sauté onions in olive oil until soft. Add bay leaf, sea salt and cover the onions with pure water. Bring to boil and reduce to simmer for 15 minutes.

(simple) Denise's Special Spinach Sausage Soup

Serves 4

½ POUND OF CHICKEN SAUSAGE

1 TABLESPOON GARLIC, CHOPPED

1 POUND OF SPINACH,
ENDS SNIPPED, COARSELY CHOPPED
OR COLLARD GREENS

THREE, 14.5 OUNCE CANS
OF CHICKEN BROTH

½ CUP OF BROKEN GLUTEN FREE PASTA

2 TEASPOONS OF PARMESAN CHEESE,
FRESHLY GRATED

Heat a large saucepot over medium high heat. Drizzle a little olive oil in pot. Add sausage and cook, stirring occasionally, until browned, about 2 minutes. Add garlic; cook 30 seconds. Add spinach and broth. Fill one empty can of broth with water; add to pot. Cover and bring mixture to a full boil.

VARIATION:
Use 1 head of escarole or kale. If using escarole, add to pot and boil 3 minutes. Add pasta, cover and boil 2 minutes more. Pour into bowls and sprinkle with Parmesan cheese.

Spinach Lentil Soup

Serves 4-6

7 CUPS OF WATER

1½ CUPS OF WASHED LENTILS

4 CLOVES CRUSHED ORGANIC GARLIC

1½ TEASPOON SEA SALT

1 LARGE RED ORGANIC ONION, CHOPPED

¼ CUP OLIVE OIL

1 POUND OF BABY SPINACH, CHOPPED

2 TABLESPOONS FRESHLY SQUEEZED
LEMON JUICE

OPTIONAL:
1 celery stalk finely chopped
*1 tablespoon arrowroot
or cornstarch*

Place lentils in a saucepan with water. Bring to boil. Cover and simmer until tender. In separate pan, brown onions and oil. Add chopped spinach, garlic, and sea salt. Mix well. Sauté slowly until spinach becomes soft, mixing in more as space becomes available. Return lentils to a boil. Add celery and sauté spinach mixture. Reduce to simmer for 5 minutes. For a thin soup, mix in desired amount of lemon juice and adjust to taste. For a thicker soup, mix in arrowroot with lemon juice before adding to the cooked soup. Allow to simmer a few minutes longer.

Roasted Winter Vegetable Soup

Serves 6

6-8 CUPS OF WATER

1 RECIPE ROASTED WINTER VEGETABLES
(See page 180)

SEA SALT

In a large saucepan, heat 6 cups of water. In two batches, coarsely purée the roasted vegetables and add the water in the bowl of a food processor fitted with the steel blade. Pour the soup back into the pot and season to taste. Thin soup with more water if necessary and reheat. The soup should be thick but not like a vegetable purée, so feel free to add more water until it's the consistency you like.

 ## Bubba's Beet Soup

Serves 6

6 MEDIUM BEETS

4 TABLESPOONS OF BUTTER

1 QUART WATER

2 TABLESPOONS OF CHOPPED CHIVES

Peel beets, and chop. Sauté in butter for ½ hour. Add water, bring to a boil and skim. Simmer for 15 minutes. Purée soup and season to taste. Add a dollop of raw sour cream.

NOTE:
Beets and their tops contain special substances that protect the liver and stimulate the flow of bile. Beet tops contain the same nutrients as the root with the added bonus of an exceptionally high carotenoid content.

 ## Watercress Soup

Serves 6

2 MEDIUM ONIONS, PEELED AND CHOPPED

3 TABLESPOONS BUTTER

1½ QUARTS OF CHICKEN BROTH
OR WATER

2 LARGE BUNCHES WATERCRESS
LEAVES, RINSED

Sauté onions gently in butter until soft. Add broth and watercress and simmer for about 10 minutes. Purée soup and add a dollop of raw cream.

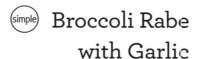

vegetables in the cabbage family

 ## Broccoli Rabe with Garlic

Serves 4

2 BUNCHES BROCCOLI RABE

3 TABLESPOONS OLIVE OIL

6 LARGE GARLIC CLOVES

Place rabe in a steamer basket for 5 minutes and then blanche for 1-2 minutes. Drain well. Heat the olive oil in a skillet. Add the garlic and broccoli rabe cooking over low heat, stirring occasionally for 4-6 minutes, until golden brown. Serve hot.

NOTE:
Maybe your grandmother was right when she told you, "Eat your vegetables." A new study (Cancer Causes Control. 2009. 20:75-86) pointed out that among dietary factors, vegetables were the only food group shown to have a favorable effect on thyroid cancer.

Broccoli with Garlic

Serves 4

2 BUNCHES BROCCOLI, CLEANED AND CHOPPED

1 LARGE ONION, CHOPPED

2 CLOVES GARLIC, MINCED

¼ CUP SAN-J® ORGANIC, GLUTEN-FREE TAMARI SOY SAUCE

1 TEASPOON GRATED PARMESAN CHEESE

Preheat oven to 350°F. Combine and place all vegetables in a covered casserole dish Mix the garlic with the tamari and pour evenly over the vegetables. Cover the dish and bake for 20-30 minutes. Sprinkle the vegetables with the Parmesan cheese. Then serve and enjoy!

(simple) ## Cabbage Sprinkled with Carrots and Sautéed Onions

Thinly slice the vegetables. Place oil over medium heat. When pan is hot, place in the vegetables and sauté for about 5-7 minutes. Serve immediately.

Serves 4-6

1 HEAD OF CABBAGE

1 CARROT, SHREDDED

1 MEDIUM ONION, CHOPPED

2 TABLESPOONS OLIVE OIL

A WORD ON CABBAGE

Cabbage is an excellent source of fiber and also boasts vitamins that are rich in B complex, vitamin C, potassium, magnesium and calcium. This special vegetable has many healing properties thanks to its abundant sulfur content. Cabbage improves digestion, treats constipation, the common cold, whooping cough, mental depression and irritability. It also contains Vitamin U—an ulcer remedy. For stomach or duodenal ulcers, drink one half cupful of freshly made cabbage juice two or three time a day between meals.
(Healing with Whole Foods, 1993)

SIMPLE TRICKS TO HELP YOU ADD MORE VEGETABLES TO YOUR DIET

Most American's today shy away from filling one half or more of their plate (double or triple serving size) with vegetables. Yet, these magnificent marvels should be the high point of your meals. They do not require much time to cook and most of them offer some benefit to the body. Almost every vegetable study conducted, shows how this food benefits the heart, blood and some even fight cancer. Steaming is the best way to cook most vegetables, but sautéing in olive oil, butter or some coconut oil is acceptable as well. The most important piece of equipment necessary for steaming your vegetables, is a steamer. You can either purchase an inexpensive steamer insert that fits inside of your pots, or you can elect to purchase an electric steamer that easily sits on your countertop.

FOURTEEN WAYS TO DISGUISE VEGETABLES IN YOUR MEALS.

The following ideas are simple suggestions to creatively add more vegetables into your diet. Play with these ideas, adding your own creative spirit. In order to save time in preparing many of the dishes below, try the following:

- *Cook up large quantities of vegetables in a steamer in the morning.*

- *Proceed to chop them and place them in plastic storage containers so they can store easily in the refrigerator.*

- *Another option is to chop up the vegetables first and then stir-fry them before storing in the refrigerator. They will remain fresh all day so that you may use them at breakfast, lunch or even dinner.*

VEGETABLE CHILI

Instead of making chili mainly with beans, substitute many more cooked vegetables such as chopped onions, garlic, broccoli, cauliflower, greens or others. You can still have turkey, lamb or beef in the chili, but it will now be much richer in vegetables.

VEGETABLE PIZZA

Children and adults seem to love pizza. Try making your own pizza with a thin, wheat free crust that can even be store-bought, if needed, followed by a thick layer of chopped up pre-cooked vegetables. Top this with some oregano or other spices, a little tomato sauce and some tasty cheese.

You also might try adding other ingredients such as chicken, turkey sausage, and even pepperoni, even though it is a processed meat. This should not be for everyday consumption, but if it helps a child or adult eat a lot more vegetables, it would be worth the time and trouble. Drawbacks of this dish are that it is a complex food combination and can disturb digestion. Also, it involves cooking the cheese, which is not optimal. It also involves tomato sauce, which is very yin and a nightshade vegetable, which is also not optimal. Once a week or so, however, might be fine for many children.

VEGETABLE ENCHILADA OR TACO

Instead of filling taco shells or enchiladas with salad, beans, or pork; fill them with chopped up cooked vegetables. One can also add a little chicken, a few sardines, cheese, a little rice or other fillings to disguise the cooked vegetables.

Always use blue or yellow organic corn tortillas, and never flour tortillas. The only disadvantage to this dish is cooking the cheese, so cook the vegetables first and then cook the enchilada minimally for best nutrition. Cheese is best eaten as raw as possible.

COOKED VEGETABLE SALAD, WITH SOME RICE PASTA OR TORTILLA CHIPS IN IT

Many children love pasta salad or taco salad. However, instead of using raw vegetables, use cooked ones such as chopped up broccoli, chopped carrots, onions, turnips, rutabagas or others. Cook the vegetables first. You can serve them hot, or let them cool down. Add a few broken blue corn chips or some rice pasta. If needed, top off the cooked salad with some fresh cheese, chopped nuts or seeds, maybe some pesto sauce or olive oil, and you have a delicious cooked taco salad. *(See page 139 for recipes)*

VEGETABLE STEWS OR CASSEROLES

This is a wonderful place to disguise vegetables. Start with some stew meat, and add chopped up vegetables. Cook in a crock-pot or in the oven until everything blends together and it all tastes like the meat. *(See page 157 for recipes)* Lamb is an excellent stew meat.

Don't overcook the meat, as it denatures the protein. The stew or casserole should cook in an hour or less, if possible. That should allow enough time to cook most vegetables as well. Otherwise, precook the vegetables if they require more time.

VEGETABLE SUSHI

For those who just cannot stay away from sushi, make some nori rolls at home filled with cooked vegetables, perhaps with a little cooked rice in them as well. One could even get creative and add mashed or whole sardines to the vegetables, along with soy sauce or other flavorings.

While nori has more toxic metals than acceptable, this would be far better than regular sushi that contains tuna, ahi, raw fish, and/or other less desirable ingredients.

VEGETABLE ENRICHED MEATLOAF

When you make a meat loaf, begin with some ground beef, ground turkey, or ground lamb. Then add a lot of pre-cooked chopped vegetables and maybe some flavoring to disguise the vegetables. If needed, add some egg to keep it from falling apart. Then bake the loaf to create an excellent family meal. *(See page 209 for recipe)*

The only drawback to meatloaves is that eggs, are needed to keep the loaf together, should preferably not be overcooked, and in fact, should be eaten mushy or soft. However, a meatloaf that is filled with vegetables is still an excellent dish.

VEGETABLE QUICHE

Vegetable quiches have been in vogue and enjoyed by many people. Simply add a whole lot of vegetables into your quiche crust, rather than a lot of cheese or a lot of anything else. *(See page 198 for recipes)* This is a favorite among many teenagers and children.

The drawbacks are that the eggs can be overcooked which is not ideal. However, once again it is far better than what most children and adults are eating today.

THICK VEGETABLE SOUPS

Adding loads of vegetables to all kinds of soups is a simple and excellent idea. For fussy eaters, disguise the vegetables by cooking them for 10-20 minutes and then purée the soup so the vegetables blend in with the rest of the soup. *(See page 161 for recipe)*

Drawbacks to soups are that having too much liquid with meals weakens digestion. So use as little water as possible, or thicken soup with arrowroot powder. Arrowroot is a much more healthful thickener than cornstarch, which will also work, if necessary. If possible, avoid using tomatoes in soups. Tomato is a nightshade vegetable that is quite irritating for the intestines, and very yin. Instead, use a base of onions, celery, or other sweet vegetables.

VEGETABLE OMELETS

Chop and cook the vegetables well. Then add the eggs and perhaps some spices to create an omelet. This is a superb dish. *(See page 199 for recipes)* While it does not disguise the vegetables, often children and adults will accept some vegetables in an omelet.

The only possible drawback to this dish is do not overcook the eggs. Try to have the omelet a little mushy, as it is best that eggs be eaten soft, not hard.

STUFFED CABBAGE, RED PEPPER, GRAPE LEAVES OR OTHER LEAVES

This is more of a fun dish that can involve the children. It does not disguise the vegetables but allows one to roll up some vegetables and rice, perhaps, in a cabbage or grape leaf and bake it into an appetizing package that can be enjoyed by all.

VEGETABLE PIE

This dish is similar to a deep dish pizza. *(See page 212 for Ava's excellent recipe.)* Begin by choosing some of your favorite vegetables and chop them up into small pieces. Use a wheat free crust and place it in your deep pie dish. Cook the crust as necessary (for about 5-10 minutes) and then begin to add in your favorite vegetables. Top it with some cheese, or perhaps a little tomato sauce. You can even put chunks of natural chicken or turkey sausage on top of your pie. Place it in the oven for about 10 minutes and wait for the cheese to bubble.

VEGETABLE FRITTERS OR OLD FASHIONED VEGETABLE PANCAKES

Some readers have had tasty vegetable fritters, or potato pancakes, perhaps. I would suggest not using potatoes. Instead, cook up some of your favorite vegetables. *(See page 182 for recipe)* Then chop up into small pieces. Mix with some egg to hold everything together, and add some seasoning if you wish. You might need other thickeners such as a little arrowroot powder. To make them sweet, you could add some cooked sweet potatoes or yams. Then place these pancakes in a frying pan in the form of fritters or pancakes with some butter or olive oil in the pan. Cook lightly on both sides for five minutes or so until they are golden brown.

ADD GREENS TO YOUR CARROT JUICE

While carrot juice is excellent, a way to cut the sweetness is to add unusual flavors, and most importantly, add more vegetables. Include a few spinach leaves, Swiss chard leaves, kale leaves, a piece of turnip, celery or rutabaga, or others. Rotate the vegetables, adding just one or two in each day's carrot juice. This is often an effective way to disguise the green vegetables.

Cauliflower Au Gratin

Serves 4

1 HEAD CAULIFLOWER,
COARSELY CHOPPED

1½ TABLESPOONS DIJON MUSTARD

½ CUP WHEAT-FREE BREAD CRUMBS

½ CUP SHREDDED CHEDDAR CHEESE

Steam the cauliflower until tender. Preheat oven to 350°F. Lightly oil a baking dish. Spread the cauliflower in the bottom of the dish. Rub on the mustard then sprinkle the cheese over the cauliflower. Sprinkle the wheat-free bread crumbs on top. Bake uncovered for 20 minutes or until the bread crumbs are lightly browned.

A WORD ON CAULIFLOWER

Cauliflower contains many nutrients that can help prevent a range of health issues from cancer to cataracts. The new varieties, purple cauliflower, or orange that you may see in your market, are higher in carotenoids, a compound that protects the cells against free radical damage.

 ## Cauliflower Whipped Up

Serves 4

1 MEDIUM HEAD OF CAULIFLOWER,
CUT INTO SMALL FLORETS

¼ CUP OF MILK

2 TABLESPOONS OF OLIVE OIL

1 TEASPOON OF SEA SALT

Place cauliflower in a steamer basket for about 8-10 minutes. Pour the milk and oil into the blender and mix. Then add in the cauliflower, and sea salt. Blend well and serve immediately.

Cornucopia of Vegetables

Serves as many as you would like

CARROTS

SWISS CHARD

CAULIFLOWER

SPINACH

BROCCOLI

PEAS

ONIONS

FRESH CORN

GARLIC

ZUCCHINI

Bake the vegetables at 350°F. Slice the vegetables into bite sized pieces and put them in a bowl. Drizzle lightly with olive oil and with your favorite spices. Place on a baking dish and cook for 20-30 minutes. If you think you might want them to be crispy, turn the oven on to broil for just a few minutes.

Fresh vegetables that are sliced and lightly oiled will bring out the savory flavors of this significant food category. Use several of these vegetables or create your own vegetable list. You can also make this dish by the season, choosing those vegetables, from winter, spring, summer and fall.

(simple) Steamed Assorted Vegetables

Serves 2-4

CHOOSE FROM A VARIETY OF VEGETABLES
(broccoli, cauliflower, cabbage)

LEMON JUICE (OPTIONAL)

DAB OF BUTTER

Place the vegetables in a steamer basket for about 5-7 minutes. When finished, remove from basket and place on plate. Dab on butter and squeeze on lemon juice as an option.

green vegetables

(simple) Asian Green Beans

Serves 4

3 CUPS OF GREEN BEANS, ENDS SNIPPED

2 TABLESPOONS OF SESAME OIL

1 CLOVE GARLIC

1 TABLESPOON OF CRUSHED GINGER

1-2 TABLESPOONS OF SAN-J® ORGANIC,
GLUTEN-FREE TAMARI SOY SAUCE

Place green beans in a steamer basket for 5 minutes. Sauté the sesame oil and crushed garlic for 2-3 minutes. Mix in the ginger and soy sauce. Stir for about 2-3 more minutes. Pour this mixture over the green beans.

NOTE:
Dr. Henry Bieler, author of "Your Food Is Your Best Medicine", highly recommended green beans for treatment of the pancreas and salivary glands because of their rich mineral content.

(simple) Jazzy Green Beans and Garlic

Serves 4

3 CUPS OF GREEN BEANS, ENDS SNIPPED

1 CLOVE GARLIC, MINCED

¼ CUP OLIVE OIL
(or try flax oil or hemp oil)

4-5 TABLESPOONS OF BALSAMIC VINEGAR

PINCH OF SEA SALT

Steam and blanch green beans. Add together in separate bowl, garlic, olive oil, vinegar and salt. Mix together and pour onto green beans. Let this marinate overnight. Next day you'll have green beans with a kick.

(simple) Roasted Asparagus with an Italian Flare

Serves 6

2 ½ POUNDS OF FRESH ASPARAGUS

2 TABLESPOONS OF OLIVE OIL

½ TEASPOON OF SEA SALT

½ CUP OF FRESHLY GRATED PARMESAN CHEESE

Preheat oven to 400°F. Lay asparagus in a single layer on a sheet pan and drizzle with olive oil. Sprinkle with sea salt. Roast for 15 minutes and then sprinkle with Parmesan cheese. Return them to the oven for another 3 minutes.

A WORD ON ASPARAGUS

There are three different varieties of asparagus farmed. Most of us are familiar with the green stalks. But did you know that there is a variety in purple, which many believe is sweeter and less stringy than the green type. There is also a white variety in which its color is achieved by restricting its exposure to sunlight. Color should be the main determinant in choosing asparagus. Ideally, the green color should be consistent from top to bottom. You know the saying that the nose knows, so go ahead and sniff those green stalks and if you smell an unpleasant odor, opt for another bunch, as that bad odor indicates old stalks.

(simple) Sautéed Kale— The Joy of Eating Green

Serves 4

4 CUPS OF SHREDDED KALE

2 TABLESPOONS OF OLIVE OIL

¼ TEASPOON OF MINCED GARLIC (OPTIONAL)

Heat up your skillet and add in the olive oil. (Add in optional garlic) Toss your kale in for about 3-4 minutes. Enjoy this nutritious vegetable.

NOTE:
Kale is an excellent source of fiber.

Simply Ratatouille

Serves 6

1½ CUPS ONIONS, DICED

1 TABLESPOON FRESH GARLIC, MINCED

1 TABLESPOON DRIED BASIL,
(fresh if in season)

5½ CUPS TOMATO PURÉE

6 CUPS EGGPLANT, CUBED

1 CUP TOMATOES, DICED

1 CUP LARGE RED BELL PEPPER, DICED

1¼ CUPS OF ¼ INCH ZUCCHINI ROUNDS

½ TEASPOON SEA SALT

Sauté the onions, garlic, and dried herbs in the olive oil. When the onions are soft and start to turn translucent, add the tomato purée. Then stir together for about 10 minutes. Add the eggplant and the red and green peppers. When these are almost cooked, add the zucchini. Do not cook the zucchini too long or it will become mushy and lose its bright color. When all the vegetables are cooked, add sea salt to taste.

NOTE:
This recipe contains nightshade vegetables that can aggravate inflammatory conditions.

 ## Spinach with Butter & Garlic

Olive Oil's Specialty

Serves 6

2 POUNDS OF CHOPPED SPINACH OR
SWISS CHARD OR KALE

1-2 TEASPOONS OF BUTTER

2 CLOVES OF FRESH GARLIC, MINCED

First, heat pan and add butter. Then add in the minced garlic and spinach. Cook for about 2-4 minutes. Cook until the leaves are wilted.

NOTE:
Feel free to try this recipe with Swiss chard and kale as well.

Many of the benefits man gets from the sunshine he can get from greens. Anyone in the city should especially think of greens as a means of getting sunshine to the body.

Dr. Bernard Jensen, from Health Magic through Chlorophyll

 ## Spring Green Vegetables

Serves 4

¼ POUND STRING BEANS

¼ POUND SNAP PEAS

¼ POUND ASPARAGUS

1 TABLESPOON OF OLIVE OIL

Steam the veggies and then immerse them in a bowl of ice water. When all the veggies are cold, drain well. When ready to serve, heat the oil in a very large sauté pan. Add the drained vegetables to the pan and toss. Cook just until the veggies are warm.

FARMER'S MARKET

Farmer's Markets are a wonderful place to shop for fresh vegetables. You are able to buy quality and a variety of seasonal vegetables, fruits and other farm fresh products. Enjoy shopping out in the fresh air and all the delights of the season.

Sweet and Sour Swiss Chard Extravaganza

Serves 4

3 CUPS OF SWISS CHARD, SLICED THIN

1 CUP OF ONIONS, MINCED

¼ CUP OF WALNUTS

10 RAISINS

2 TABLESPOONS OF BUTTER

In a large skillet, sauté the onions until they brown. Then add in the walnuts and raisins. Cook for 5 more minutes. Then add in the Swiss chard. Cook all the ingredients together for an additional 5-7 minutes. This is delicious served over brown rice.

NOTE:
Farmer's Markets are a wonderful place to shop for fresh vegetables. You are able to buy quality and a variety of seasonal vegetables, fruits and other farm fresh products. Enjoy shopping out in the fresh air and all the delights of the season.

Vegetables with a Thai Accent

Serves 4

2 CLOVES OF GARLIC, FINELY CHOPPED

1 TEASPOON OF GINGER, MINCED

1 CUP CARROT JUICE

4 CUPS OF MIXED VEGETABLES
(Be creative and choose your favorite options)

4 TABLESPOONS RAW CASHEWS

¼ TEASPOON OF CURRY POWDER

1 TABLESPOON PEANUT OR ALMOND BUTTER

¼ CUP OF COCONUT MILK *(unsweetened)*

Add garlic, ginger, carrot juice, vegetables, two tablespoons of cashews and curry powder to a large wok or skillet. Stir until all vegetables are cooked. Mix in nut butter. Add coconut milk and heat through. Sprinkle on the remaining cashews.

root vegetables

 ### Baked Garlic

Serves 4

4 HEADS OF GARLIC

OLIVE OIL

SEA SALT

Preheat oven to 300°F. Peel off the outer skin of the garlic. Then place the garlic in a baking dish. Sprinkle with sea salt and drizzle olive oil over the garlic. Add in a small amount of water to just barely cover the bottom of the baking dish. Cover and bake for about 1 hour. Enjoy this by itself.

NOTE:
You could also pick up some fresh goat cheese. Place the garlic on a slice of goat cheese. It is delicious.

Golden Beets Galore

Serves 4

5-6 GOLDEN BEETS

¼ CUP OLIVE OIL

1 TEASPOON APPLE CIDER VINEGAR

1 CLOVE GARLIC, MINCED

1 TEASPOON OREGANO

FETA CHEESE (OPTIONAL)

Steam or boil beets until easy to insert fork. This takes about 30-40 minutes. Peel beets and cut into ¼ inch cubes. Combine olive oil, vinegar, garlic and oregano. Pour over beets.

VARIATION:
Add feta cheese. Make extra of this fabulous dish because it is great after marinating overnight.

A WORD ON BEETS
Beets play an important role in protecting against colon cancer. Beets and their tops contain special compounds that protect the liver and help to stimulate the flow of bile. Make sure when you shop for beets that you purchase beets with their long green tops as that is an excellent indication of their freshness. Additionally, those beet greens contain an added bonus of caroteinoids, which protects the cells from the damaging effects of free radicals, and is delicious when washed and trimmed into thin slices, and sautéed in olive oil. You can eat these greens separately, or you can mix them in with your beets. Give it a try!

Baked Onion Flowers

Serves 4

4 MEDIUM ONIONS, SLICED LENGTHWISE

2 TABLESPOONS OF BUTTER

ADD SEA SALT AS NEEDED

Preheat the oven to 350°F. Place the sliced onions in a casserole dish. Dot with butter and sprinkle on sea salt. Cook for about 45 minutes.

 # Grill or Broil Those Onion Rings

Serves 4

4 MEDIUM ONIONS

BUTTER

SEA SALT

Slice onions lengthwise and brush with butter. Place on grill or in the oven on broil. Cook for about 5 minutes per side. Add sea salt as needed.

Roasted Winter Vegetables

Serves 6

1 POUND PARSNIPS,

1 LARGE SWEET POTATO

1 SMALL BUTTERNUT SQUASH, PEELED AND SEEDED

3 TABLESPOONS OF OLIVE OIL

1 TEASPOON OF SEA SALT *(coarse type)*

2 TABLESPOONS FRESH FLAT LEAF PARSLEY, CHOPPED

ADD SEA SALT AS NEEDED

Preheat the oven to 425°F. Cut the carrots, parsnips, sweet potato and butternut squash into 1 inch cubes. All the vegetables will shrink while baking, so do not cut them too small. Place all the veggies in a single layer on two sheet pans. Drizzle them with olive oil and salt. Toss well. Bake for 25-35 minutes until all the veggies are tender, turning them once with a spatula. Sprinkle with parsley, season to taste and serve hot.

NOTE:
The high temperature required in this recipe caramelizes the outside of the vegetables and leaves the inside tender and moist. This is a very flexible recipe; you can add any root vegetable you have available to this mélange.

Rooting for What?
Rutabagas

Serves 4

1 POUND OF RUTABAGAS

SEA SALT

2 TABLESPOONS OF BUTTER (OPTIONAL)

Scrub and peel if desired. The peels are nutritious, but can be bitter. If the rutabaga is large, cut in quarters, slice or try cutting them in French fry fashion. Place them into your steamer and let them cook for about 20-30 minutes. Season them with butter if you would like, and sea salt.

VARIATION:
When your rutabagas are done steaming, you can mash them and serve with a dollop of butter.

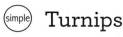 # Turnips

Serves 4

1 POUND OF TURNIPS

2 TABLESPOONS OF BUTTER (OPTIONAL)

SEA SALT

PARSLEY

Scrub and peel if desired. If the turnip is large, you can slice them, cut in quarters or try cutting them in French fry fashion. Otherwise, place them into your steamer. Let them cook for about 20-30 minutes or until they are tender. Add the butter if you would like, parsley and sea salt to taste.

VARIATION:
When your turnips are done steaming, you can mash them and serve with a dollop of butter.

NOTE:
Turnips are a rich source of calcium, phosphorus, folic acid and magnesium. Did you know that in medieval times, doctors used this unpopular vegetable to help with toothaches, stomach aches and impotence?

Winter Vegetable Casserole

Serves 4

2 MEDIUM SWEET POTATOES, SLICED

1 MEDIUM PARSNIP, SLICED

6 OUNCES OF PUMPKIN, SLICED

1 TABLESPOON OF BUTTER

1 CUP OF MILK

½ TEASPOON OF NUTMEG

TOPPING:

3 OUNCES OF ROASTED CASHEW NUTS, ROUGHLY CHOPPED

1 TABLESPOON OF BUTTER

Preheat oven to 350°F. Cut sweet potatoes, parsnips and pumpkin into large-bite sized pieces. Cook vegetables in a large pan of boiling water for 8 minutes or until tender. Drain and then arrange cooked vegetables in a base of a large, deep baking dish. Melt butter in a pan over low heat. Add in the milk, the nutmeg, and sea salt and pour over the vegetables. Bake in oven for 15-20 minutes.

TOPPING:
Sprinkle the cashews over the vegetables. Dot the topping with a bit of butter.

NOTE:
The sweet potato has a very high beta carotene content, which is helpful in protecting against cancer, colds, and infections.

Grandma's Heavenly Zucchini Pancakes

Serves 6

2 MEDIUM ZUCCHINIS *(about ¾ pound)*

2 TABLESPOONS ONION, CHOPPED

2 EXTRA-LARGE EGGS, LIGHTLY BEATEN

6 TO 8 TABLESPOONS GLUTEN FREE FLOUR

1 TEASPOON BAKING POWDER

3 TEASPOONS OF SEA SALT

UNSALTED BUTTER

Grate the zucchini into a bowl using the large grating side of a box grater. Then place two teaspoons of sea salt on the zucchini and let sit for one hour. Wrap the grated zucchini in a cheesecloth and then strain to remove the remaining liquid. Immediately stir in the onion and eggs. Stir in 6 tablespoons of the gluten free flour, baking powder, and the remaining sea salt. (If the batter gets too thin from the liquid in the zucchini, add the remaining 2 tablespoons of flour.) Heat a large (10 to 12-inch) sauté pan over medium heat and melt 1 tablespoon butter in the pan. Drop heaping spoons of batter into the pan. Cook the pancakes about 2 minutes on each side, until browned. Serve hot.

grains and legumes

Blissful Lentil Pasta Stew

Serves 4

2 TABLESPOONS OLIVE OIL

1 LARGE CLOVE OF GARLIC

1 SMALL ONION, FINELY CHOPPED

2 LARGE CARROTS, CHOPPED

1 CUP OF GREEN LENTILS

3 CUPS OF WATER

1 CUP OF MARINARA SAUCE

PINCH OF SEA SALT

1 CUP OF BROWN RICE PASTA ELBOWS

Heat oil in a 4 quart pan. Sauté vegetables. Add lentils, water, sauce and seasonings. Bring to boil. Lower to medium heat and cook covered for 1 hour. Add in cooked brown rice pasta. Remove from stove and serve with an optional garnish of crumbled Feta cheese.

NOTE:
This dish contains tomatoes, a member of the nightshade family, which can aggravate inflammatory conditions.

Brian's Mix n' Match Quinoa

Serves 4

1 CUP OF QUINOA

¼ CUP OF SWEET ONION, CHOPPED

¼ CUP OF APPLES, CHOPPED

2 TABLESPOONS OF BUTTER

FOOD FACT
Although many of us think of quinoa as a grain, it is actually a seed. It is a wonderful food that is nutritious and its protein quality is superior to other grains.

First, soak the quinoa for about 15 minutes. (This helps to loosen the saponin, which can give the quinoa a bitter taste if not removed.) Drain the water. Place the 1 cup of quinoa into 2 cups of water with a pinch of sea salt. Bring to a boil and cover the pot with a tight fitting lid. Turn down the heat to a simmer and cook for 20 minutes. Remove from the heat and allow to sit for five minutes. While waiting for the quinoa to cool, melt butter in a medium size pan. Sauté the onions and apples for about 5-7 minutes. Mix the onions and chopped apples into quinoa. Fluff gently with a fork and serve.

Quinoa Fit for a Queen with Roasted Vegetables

Serves 6-8

3 BEETS, 1 RED AND 1 GOLDEN, STEAMED AND SLICED

4 CARROTS, STEAMED AND CHOPPED

3 PARSNIPS, STEAMED AND CHOPPED

2 TABLESPOONS OF PARSLEY, CHOPPED

1 CUP QUINOA

SEA SALT TO TASTE

Place beets, carrots and parsnips into a steamer basket. Steam vegetables for about 30-40 minutes or until done. Then remove the beets, carrots and turnips from the steaming basket and let cool. Chop and slice the vegetables. In a new pot, place 1 cup of quinoa and add 2 cups of water. Bring to a boil, and then lower heat to simmer, cover and cook for 10-15 minutes, until quinoa is tender. Remove from heat and set aside to let cool to room temperature. Put quinoa and roasted carrots, parsnips and beets into a large bowl. Toss to combine. Add in parsley and sea salt to taste.

NOTE:
This is a dish that can be prepared in advance. If you want to freeze this dish, just separate the quinoa and the vegetables into their own containers. When ready to use, defrost and toss them together.

Brown Rice Parmesan Wendy's Trouble Free Dish

Serves 4

1 CUP BROWN RICE

¼ CUP OF PARMESAN CHEESE, GRATED

1 TABLESPOON OF BUTTER

SEA SALT TO TASTE

Cook 1 cup brown rice in 2 cups of water. Bring to a boil then simmer for approximately 40-60 minutes with pot covered. When rice is done, add in butter, Parmesan cheese, and salt to taste.

Fried Rice Plus Vegetables

Serves 8

2 CUPS BROWN RICE

2 CUPS FRESH VEGETABLES, CHOPPED
(ZUCCHINI, MUSHROOMS, CARROTS,
MUNG SPROUTS, PEAS)

1 SMALL ONION, FINELY CHOPPED

2 EGGS, LIGHTLY BEATEN

2 TEASPOONS OLIVE OIL

3 TEASPOONS SEA SALT

OPTIONAL:
Add in fresh chopped ginger, garlic and a dash of
tamari to tantalize your taste buds.

First, cook two cups of brown rice in four cups of water. Bring rice and water to a boil then simmer for 40-60 minutes in a covered pot. In a large pan, heat oil on medium-high heat. Add onions and rice. Stir and cook until the onion is soft, about 5 minutes. Reduce heat to medium and add vegetables to rice mixture. Cook for an additional 5-7 minutes. Spread the mixture out to the sides of the pan, leaving space in the middle for the eggs. Add the eggs, and scramble until cooked firm. Mix the eggs with the rice and vegetables then sprinkle with salt.

NOTE:
This is great to eat as leftovers for the next day.

VARIATION:
Instead of using sea salt, try seasoning this dish with tamari.

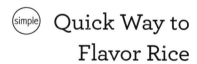 # Quick Way to Flavor Rice

Serves 4

1 CUP OF BROWN RICE

2 TABLESPOONS OF OLIVE OIL

½ OF AN ONION, MINCED

SEASON TO TASTE:
CUMIN, OR CORIANDER AND
TOASTED ALMONDS

First, cook 1 cup of brown rice in 2 cups of water. Bring rice and water to a boil, then simmer for 40-60 minutes in a covered pot. Sauté the onion in olive oil. Add in cumin or coriander. Mix into cooked rice.

VARIATION:
Sprinkle on toasted almonds.

Sinfully Delicious Lentils and Tomatoes

Serves 4

2 TEASPOONS EXTRA VIRGIN OLIVE OIL

2 CUPS LARGE YELLOW ONIONS, DICED

2 CUPS LARGE CARROTS, DICED

1 TABLESPOON GARLIC, MINCED

ONE, 28 OUNCE CAN OF PLUM TOMATOES, CHOPPED

1 CUP OF GREEN LENTILS

2 CUPS OF WATER

PINCH OF SEA SALT

Heat the oil in a large saucepan. Add the onions and carrots and cook over medium low heat for 8-10 minutes, until the onions start to brown and smell delightful. Stir occasionally. Add the garlic and cook for about 1-2 more minutes. Add the tomatoes, lentils and water to the pan. Raise the heat to bring to a boil, and then lower the heat and simmer covered for about 1 hour or until the lentils are tender. Check occasionally to be sure the liquid is still simmering. Remove from the heat and allow the lentils to sit covered for another 10 minutes.

VARIATION:
If you would like to spice this up a bit, try adding in some curry powder.

NOTE:
This dish contains tomatoes, a member of the nightshade family that can aggravate inflammatory conditions.

Chinese Proverb: Whatever the father of illness, the mother is wrong food.

An Apple a Day, Keeps the Doctor Away....

Decadent Baked Apple Surprise

Serves 6

6 LARGE BAKING APPLES

2 CUPS OF WATER

½ CUP OF ALMOND SLICES OR
½ CUP OF CRUSHED WALNUTS

½ TEASPOON OF CINNAMON

Core the apples and place in a baking pan. Sprinkle cinnamon on the top of the apple. Place 2 cups of water in the bottom of the pan. Place in oven and bake at 325°F for about 2 hours or until apples are tender. Remove from oven and while the apples are hot, sprinkle crushed walnuts or sliced almonds on top of the apples. Serve hot or cold. For a special treat, add a dollop of yogurt to the apple.

VARIATION:
For those who would like their apple a bit sweeter, top your apple with a teaspoon of honey or agave nectar.

 ## Baked Ricotta Cheese

Serves 6

1 POUND OF RICOTTA CHEESE

OPTIONAL:

Berries
Nuts
Real vanilla
Cinnamon

Preheat oven to 350°F. Mix in one or all of the optional ingredients with the ricotta cheese. Place the mixture in an ungreased glass pie pan. Spread in pan and make a circle shape that is about 6 inches in diameter and about ½ inch thick. Bake for about 30-35 minutes until the edges turn brown. Cool to room temperature and then cut into wedges. Sprinkle with one, some or all the optional ingredients.

(simple) Bake Them Up! Hotsy-Totsy Tortillas

Serves 3-4

6 CORN TORTILLAS

2 TABLESPOONS OF BUTTER

SEA SALT TO TASTE

Brush tortillas with melted butter and arrange them on cookie sheets. Then place these tortillas in a 250°F oven. Bake several hours until crisp. May be broken into chips.

(simple) Corn Bread

Serves 4

1¼ CUPS OF CORNMEAL

¼ TEASPOON BAKING SODA

1 TEASPOON SEA SALT

1 CUP OF COOKED CORN

1 EGG

1 CUP BUTTERMILK

¼ CUP OF HIGH QUALITY UNREFINED COCONUT OIL

Preheat oven to 400°F. Pour ingredients into a bowl and mix together. Pour into a greased baking pan. Bake for 20 minutes. Let the corn bread cool and then slice.

NOTE:
My family loves this recipe! The coconut oil gives this corn bread a naturally sweet flavor.

FUN CORN FACT

The Journal of Agriculture and Food Chemistry (2008) states that there are significant health benefits to milled yellow corn products such as cornmeal. Milled corn products are rich in antioxidants, and especially carotenoids—known for the prevention of chronic diseases.

Dippity Dips

Serves 4

½ CUP OF FULL FAT PLAIN YOGURT

½ CUP OF FULL FAT SOUR CREAM

¼ CUP OF DILL

½ TEASPOON OF SALT

Mix all the ingredients together and put into the refrigerator to chill for about 1 hour. Garnish your plate with cucumber slices, carrot sticks, celery sticks and green beans and begin dipping. Enjoy!

VARIATION:
Try substituting other fresh herbs to this easy to make dip. For example, cumin, curry powder or turmeric will create an Indian flavored dip. Feel free to be creative and try your hand at accenting your dip with other spices.

Make Your Own Pesto

Serves about 4

2 TABLESPOONS OF WALNUT PIECES

1 CUP BASIL LEAVES

1 TEASPOON GARLIC MINCED

¼ CUP MILK

PARMESAN CHEESE

Combine all the ingredients in a blender. Process on high speed until smooth—1-2 minutes. Pour into an airtight container and refrigerate. It will last up to 3 days.

Those who act with bravery and courage will overcome disease, while those who act out of fear will fall ill.

Inner Classic

(simple) Hot and Fast Pesto Cheese Dip

Serves about 8

8 OUNCES OF CREAM CHEESE
¼ CUP OF PESTO
(you can make your own see page 189 or purchase ready made from the market)
BLUE CORN CHIPS OR
BAKED TORTILLA CHIPS

Mix the cream cheese and basil pesto together in a food processor or in a blender.

Serve with chips on the side.

No Ho-Hum Hummus

Servings 6

2 LARGE GARLIC CLOVES
ONE, 15 ½ OUNCE CAN OF GARBANZO BEANS + ¼ CUP OF LIQUID FROM THE CAN
¼ CUP OF FRESH LEMON JUICE
1½ TABLESPOONS OF TAHINI
¼ CUP OF OLIVE OIL
SEA SALT TO TASTE

In a food processor with the metal blade attached, fine chop the garlic. Add the garbanzo beans to the bowl with the lemon juice and red pepper flakes. Process the mixture until smooth and creamy. With the motor running, add the oil through the feed tube in a steady stream. Then add in ¼ cup of the liquid and blend on low for 3-5 minutes. Scrape down the side of the bowl and add salt and process again until smooth. Transfer to a bowl and cover. Refrigerate 2 hours or preferably overnight so all the flavors meld. Keeps about 4 days. (If it lasts that long!)

A WORD ON CAFFEINE

Coffee contains some caffeine, a mild but harmful stimulant. Stimulants whip the adrenal glands into action. This eventually weakens the adrenals and perhaps the thyroid gland leading to more depletion of a person's energy. In large enough amounts, or with chronic use, caffeine from any source is associated with anxiety, irritability, tremors, and rebound fatigue and exhaustion.

Pumpkin Pie/Pudding

Makes 2 pies

3 CUPS PUMPKIN PURÉE

⅓ CUP HONEY

2 TABLESPOONS OF BLACKSTRAP MOLASSES

3 TEASPOONS CINNAMON

1 TEASPOON SEA SALT

4 EGGS, SLIGHTLY BEATEN

2 CUPS SCALDED MILK

Mix in order given. Pour into gluten-free pie shell and bake 10 minutes at 450°F then 40 minutes at 350°F or until set.

VARIATION:
Pour pumpkin mix into a buttered dish and bake as pumpkin pudding or add to a gluten-free pie shell for pumpkin pie.

SUN TEA: WANT TO ADD SOME SUNSHINE TO YOUR LIFE?

Choose a clear glass jar that can hold the amount of tea you want to make. (This jar should have a working lid.) Fill the jar with cold spring water. Choose your herbal tea. Place the tea bags in the water. You can use loose teas as well. Just put them in a tea ball or cheesecloth. Close the lid. Place jar in the sun. In an hour, check the tea's strength and color. If you chose to use loose tea without a container, strain the tea. Pour over ice and enjoy.

NOTE:
Please skip the sugar. Did you know that a typical 12 ounce soda has about 10 teaspoons of sugar? Water has no sugar. Replacing one soda daily with water or Sun Tea (unsweetened) can cut 3,650 teaspoons of sugar a year from your diet. Make good choices for yourself and your family.

JUICING

Fresh vegetable juices are nutrient packed cleansers and tonics that invigorate the body. They are a wonderful addition to your lifestyle, but are just one aspect of improving your health. The benefits of juicing are best obtained by synthesizing these fantastic juices with a healthy nutrient rich diet, excellent lifestyle and gentle exercise. By adding nutrient rich vegetable juice to your wholesome and balanced diet, you can enhance the process of restoring essential nutrients to the depleted cells in the body. Below you will find some very important reasons, why integrating vegetable juicing into your nutritional balancing program, will help to optimize your vitality. In fact, research has shown that juicing provides your body with an assortment of nutrients, enzymes, vitamins and minerals in a manner that allows your body to absorb these nutrients into the bloodstream within 30 minutes of drinking.

WHEN YOU JUICE VEGETABLES, IT MAKES IT EASIER TO ABSORB THE NUTRIENTS. *Most people today have impaired digestion, due to poor eating habits and less than ideal food choices. Consequently, your body is unable to assimilate all the nutrients from your foods. Juicing aids digestion because the juice is in a more bio-available form to optimize assimilation of nutrients.*

MORE VEGETABLES CAN EASILY BE ADDED TO THE DIET. *If you find eating vegetables difficult, juicing can make this easier for you. A glass of carrot juice can be comprised of 6 carrots, already helping you increase your intake of veggies in an efficient way.*

FRESH VEGETABLE JUICE IS FILLED WITH AN IMPORTANT GROUP OF NU-TRIENTS CALLED ENZYMES. *Enzymes, your body's work force, are catalysts that assist in thousands of chemical reactions that are essential to diges-tion, absorption, conversion into cellular tissues and energy produc-tion at the cellular level. This group of nutrients is crucial to most metabolic activity occurring in the body daily.*

JUICING GREEN VEGETABLES LIKE WHEATGRASS OR KALE IS A WON-DERFUL MEANS OF DETOXIFYING THE BODY. *The chlorophyll in these green wonders help the body remove toxins, detoxify the liver and rebuild blood cells.*

JUICING PROVIDES ORGANIC MINERALS. *Easily assimilated are calcium and potassium, two of the many minerals found in freshly juiced vegetables. These minerals help to re-store the biochemical mineral balance at the cellular level, which can help to prevent premature aging of cells.*

JUICING TIPS

- *Whenever you can, use organically grown, unsprayed produce to make the healthiest juice possible.*

- *Before juicing, wash all produce well and remove moldy and bruised or other damaged portions of the vegetables.*

HOW TO START JUICING

First, purchase a quality juicer. I recommend a Champion Juicer™. Next, try to purchase the freshest, high quality organic carrots.

1. *Wash the carrots and trim the ends.*

2. *Push carrots through the juicer and catch the juice in a bowl or cup.*

3. *Drink juice immediately.*

TIP: It is not necessary to peel carrots, but if they are not organic, you might want to take off the skin to reduce exposure to pesticides. You can also run a small piece of ginger (about 1 inch) through the juicer for a bit of zest in your juice.

TOOLS NEEDED TO JUICE YOUR VEGGIES

Vegetables
Chef's knives
Peeler
Vegetable brushes
Vegetable Juicer

HOW TO JUICE WHEATGRASS

First, you will need a serrated knife or pair of scissors, several bowls, shot glasses, measuring cups and a juicer.

Next, wheatgrass juicers are manual hand-cranked or electric. Electric juicers should be low rpm (not over 50 rpm) because high speed oxidizes the grass and the grass fibers bind. Don't even try to use a blender. Electric juicers are the only expensive part of this whole process. Hand-cranked models are cheaper but you have to do some work to make your juice.

NOW, THE JUICING BEGINS...

1. *Harvest the wheatgrass with scissors or a knife. Hold a bunch of wheatgrass in one hand and cut as close to the soil as possible with the other hand. Have a bowl handy.*

2. *Get the juicer out. You will need a bowl to catch the expelled pulp and shot-glasses or measuring cups to hold the juice. Feed the grass into the hopper and either crank or let electricity do the work. Soon a dark green liquid will come out with the pulp coming out separately. The pulp can be run through the juicer again. A light green foam comes out as well making a head on the juice.*

3. *Clean the juicer right away. It is difficult to clean if left too long.*

④ After harvest you have a tray full of grass stubble. There are plenty of things to do with it. Continue to water it and get a second growth to juice again. It is a good addition to compost bins and worm bins. Break the mat of the roots and soil into pieces before adding to the bin. You can also feed it to chickens. They love pecking out the berry and getting some fresh greens at the same time. Take the mat of roots, soil and grass stubble out in one piece for the chickens.

The juice should be used within 30 minutes of harvest and juicing. It starts to break down and go bad within 12 hours.

MAKING ALMOND & RICE MILK

Making Almond Milk
Soak almonds overnight and then grind them up or blend them into a drink. Grinding them and then adding water is probably slightly better than blending them. Grinding exposes them to a little less air. Then add a multi-vitamin/mineral for children and fish or flaxseed oil, at the very least.

Making Rice Milk
Cook rice for at least two hours and then add water for consistency. Add a multi-vitamin/mineral for children and fish or flaxseed oil, at the very least.

LUNCH BOX SPECIALS & PACKABLE SNACKS FOR CHILDREN/ADULTS OF ALL AGES

- Celery and nut butters

- Mozzarella or Cheddar cheese sticks

- Rolled slices of turkey or chicken breast with a carrot on the inside

- Trail Mix-Nuts mixtures- with a natural corn flake or wheat free cereal. (Check ingredients in trail nut mixtures as many contain sugary items.)

- Blue Corn Chips with peanut butter or hummus.

- Plain/Vanilla Organic Yogurts. (You can mix these together so there is less sugar)

- Cut up veggies with hummus or yogurt dip with fresh herbs mixed in,

- Celery and Almond Butter- you can try other nut butters as well

- Natural Turkey Jerky or Beef Jerky

- Almond butter balls rolled in puffed rice cereal

- Thermos filled with hot soups or chili.

- Organic apple with almond butter

- Quinoa tabouli with blue corn chips

salad dressings

Best Salad Dressing!

Variation 1:

½ CUP EXTRA VIRGIN OLIVE OIL OR
FLAX OIL *(expeller pressed)*

¼ CUP FRESH LEMON JUICE
(ABOUT 1 LARGE LEMON)

¼ CUP FRESH PARSLEY,
ROUGHLY CHOPPED

1 TEASPOON GARLIC, MINCED

SEA SALT TO TASTE

¾ CUP EXTRA VIRGIN OLIVE OIL OR
FLAX OIL *(expeller pressed)*

¼ CUP LEMON JUICE

1 TABLESPOON SHALLOTS, MINCED

Variation 2:

½ CUP EXTRA VIRGIN OLIVE OIL
(expeller pressed)
*(flax oil or hemp oil are great alternatives
to olive oil)*

¼ CUP LEMON JUICE

1 TABLESPOON SHALLOTS, MINCED

SEA SALT TO TASTE

Balsamic Dressing

1 TEASPOON DIJON-TYPE MUSTARD

2 TABLESPOONS BALSAMIC VINEGAR

½ CUP EXTRA VIRGIN OLIVE OIL

1 TABLESPOON EXPELLER EXPRESSED
FLAX OIL

Mix all ingredients together and
use immediately.

Basic Dressing

1 TEASPOON DIJON-TYPE MUSTARD,
SMOOTH OR GRAINY

2 TABLESPOONS OF APPLE CIDER VINEGAR

½ CUP EXTRA VIRGIN OLIVE OIL

1 TABLESPOON OF EXPELLER EXPRESSED
FLAX OIL

Mix together and use immediately.

*VARIATION: Feel free, to use fresh herbs
such as chopped basil, parsley or oregano
with the above dressings. You could also add
in fresh garlic to any of these savory mixtures.*

*NOTE: Do not use flax or hemp oil for cook-
ing. Oils high in essential fatty acids are
not good for cooking. Heat can turn these
healthy fats into harmful ones. Keep your flax
oil and hemp oil in the refrigerator. This oil
can turn rancid in about 6 weeks, so purchase small bottles.*

recipes for children

ENJOYED BY EVERYONE

COOKING FOR KIDS - AND FOR THE KID IN ALL OF US

Preparing food for kids is a cinch with the simple recipes provided in this section. For many of us, we are searching for magical foods that will not only delight our young ones, but also provide them with excellent nutrition that is nourishing and wholesome.

Incorporating foods that will infuse their bodies with superb fuel can be challenging, given their hyped-up romance with junk food and fast foods. There are many options that are nutritious, healthful and wholesome that you can prepare to help your children make excellent food choices. For instance, in this chapter, you will find some of my favorite and quick recipes that my own children love. Try out The Deviled Egg Made Me Do It!, or Brian's Tortilla Cigars. Your wee ones, might even love the Mexican Nacho Hat Dance or Mighty Healthy Meatloaf. And for the adults, this section is for you too—for the kid in all of us.

breakfast eggs

(simple) ## Billy the Kid Goat Cheese Omelet with Fresh Dill

Serves 1

TWO ½ INCH SLICES OF GOAT CHEESE
2 EGGS
1 TABLESPOON OF FRESH DILL
1 TABLESPOON OF BUTTER
PINCH OF SEA SALT

In a small bowl, mix the goat cheese with the dill. Use a fork to mash the ingredients together. Set aside. Then, in another small bowl, mix the eggs and sea salt. Melt butter in a small sized pan. When the butter is melted, add in the eggs and let them begin to set. Lift the edges of the egg and let the uncooked egg cook through as you tilt the pan. When the eggs looks done, drop the goat cheese mixture over one half of the omelet. Slide the spatula under the other half and cover the mixture. Let it cook for about 3 more minutes, then slide the omelet out of the pan. Feel free to garnish with some berries.

(simple) ## Breakfast Pizza

Serves 1

1 BROWN RICE TORTILLA
2-3 TABLESPOONS OF WHOLE MILK RAW COTTAGE CHEESE
¼ CUP SHREDDED MOZZARELLA CHEESE

Place tortilla on a clean surface and spoon on cottage cheese to the tortilla. Gently spread cottage cheese with a spoon to cover the tortilla. Sprinkle on the mozzarella cheese on top of the cottage cheese. Place in the toaster oven or conventional oven at 350°F until the cheese is bubbling.

VARIATION:
Try sprinkling on shredded vegetables to this delightful breakfast food.

RAW MILK
Raw, certified milk and cheese comes from cows that are pastured, containing all the fat and has not been processed, pasteurized and homogenized. Pasteurization destroys important enzymes, diminishes vitamin content, and kills beneficial bacteria. Raw milk sours naturally, while pasteurized milk turns rancid. California, Connecticut, and New Mexico are a few states that sell raw milk products in the market. In other states, you can purchase raw milk through a farm where you cow-share. (www.realmilk.com-all about raw milk)

Mothers in the nutrition education network of Washington's focus groups said, "when we eat together we eat better."

Everything But the Kitchen Sink... Quiche

Serves 4-6

1 GLUTEN FREE PIE SHELL

4 EGGS

CUP OF MILK

½ CUP OF HEAVY CREAM

¼ TEASPOON OF SEA SALT

¼ CUP OF ZUCCHINI

¼ CUP OF PEAS

¼ CUP OF ONIONS

½ CUP OF GRATED CHEDDAR CHEESE

Mix all the ingredients together and pour into the pie shell. Bake at 375°F for about 40-45 minutes or until firm. Take out from oven and let cool for about 2-3 minutes. Serve with some carrot sticks and dip on the side.

NOTE:
Below is a basic recipe for quiche so you can create your own special dish. Feel free to add in a variety of vegetables, meats and cheeses.

 ## Basic Quiche Recipe

Serves 6

1 GLUTEN FREE PIE SHELL

4 EGGS

1 CUP OF MILK

¼ CUP OF HEAVY CREAM

¼ TEASPOON OF SEA SALT

Mix all the ingredients together and pour into the pie shell. Bake at 375°F, for about 40-45 minutes or until firm. Take out from oven and let cook for about 2-3 minutes.

Be creative and enjoy. You can even name your own quiche. Get your children involved and ask them to come up with some ingredients and a name for their new recipe.

Mama Joy's Green Eggs—No Ham

Serves 2

1 POUND OF BABY SPINACH

3 TABLESPOONS OF MILK

4 EGGS

PINCH OF SEA SALT

TURKEY BACON *(1-2 slices)*

BUTTER

Melt butter in a medium sized pan. Add the spinach and turn the heat to high until the spinach wilts. Add in the milk and cook until it evaporates. Place these ingredients into a food processor or Magic Bullet™ and make a purée. Let cool. Mix the eggs and melt the butter in a pan. Mix all the ingredients together and cook on low to medium heat. Stir occasionally until done. Add some turkey bacon on the side. Enjoy!

Special Scrambled Eggs Mi Amigo!

Serves 1-2

2 LARGE EGGS

¼ CUP OF SOUR CREAM

½ CUP OF CAULIFLOWER PURÉE

2 TABLESPOONS OF FRESH PARMESAN CHEESE

PINCH OF SEA SALT

BUTTER

In a bowl whisk together the eggs, sour cream, cauliflower purée, Parmesan cheese and sea salt. Then slowly add in the egg mixture. Stir all ingredients together. Melt butter in pan. Pour the ingredients into the pan. Slowly stir the mixture over low to medium heat making sure the eggs are scrambled. Enjoy!

CALCIUM RICH FOODS

Excellent sources of calcium-rich foods include raw, certified milk, cheese and yogurt. Others include, carrot juice, sardines, and egg yolks. Soups made with bones of lamb, chicken or veal joints are also excellent ways to include more calcium in your diet. You can also check out kelp, sea vegetables, almonds, Sesame seeds, and dark green vegetables such as kale and turnip greens.

(simple)

Herbed Eggs in a Blanket

Serves 2

4 EGGS

2 TABLESPOONS OF MILK

1 TEASPOON OF BASIL

1-2 TABLESPOONS OF BUTTER

PINCH OF SEA SALT

2 CORN TORTILLAS

Scramble the eggs in a bowl adding in milk, basil and sea salt. Melt 1 tablespoon of butter in a medium sized pan. Pour egg batter in and cook on low-medium heat. Stir eggs gently. In a separate large pan, melt 1 tablespoon of butter and place the two corn tortillas in the pan and lightly brown both sides. When the eggs are done, place them on the tortillas and roll them up. Your eggs are now in their blanket.

NOTE:
Many believe that eating fat makes fat. However fat does not make fat in the body. A healthy body must have fat to carry on its important processes. Carbohydrates, grains, breads, starches and sugars are the foods that make fat and it is these foods that must be removed from the diets of people who have weight issues.

That Deviled Egg Made Me Do It!

Serves 6

6 LARGE EGGS

3 TABLESPOONS OF MAYONNAISE

1 TABLESPOON OF MUSTARD

¼ CUP OF CAULIFLOWER OR CARROT PURÉE

PINCH OF SEA SALT

SPRINKLE OF PAPRIKA

Boil the eggs for about 15 minutes. Drain eggs and cool these devils under very cold running water. Cut eggs lengthwise and remove egg yolk. Mash the yolks with a fork. Then, add the mayonnaise, mustard, vegetable purée and salt, mixing all the ingredients together. Fill each egg half with the yolk mixture. Sprinkle on paprika.

NOTE:
Eggs are great for your eyes, due to the carotenoid content. (Carotenoids play a role as antioxidants in the body). Also contains vitamin D and promotes healthy hair and nails.

One Frittata, Two Frittata, Three Frittata, Four

Serves 4 or more

¼ CUP OF OLIVE OIL

1 ONION, FINELY CHOPPED

1 SMALL CARROT, GRATED

1 SMALL ZUCCHINI, GRATED

1 CUP PUMPKIN, PURÉED

½ INCH SLICE OF GOAT CHEESE

½ TEASPOON SEA SALT

5 EGGS

Heat 2 tablespoons of olive oil in a frying pan. Add the onion and cook gently for 5 minutes or until onions are soft. Add the carrot, zucchini and pumpkin; cover the pan and cook over low heat for 3 minutes. Transfer the mixture to a bowl and cool. Stir in goat cheese, and sea salt. Beat the eggs and add them to the vegetables in the mixture. Heat the remaining oil in a small frying pan. When the oil is hot, add the egg mixture to the pan and shake the pan to spread the mixture evenly over the base. Reduce the heat to low and cook for 3 minutes or until mixture is set almost all the way through. Tilt pan and lift the edges of frittata occasionally during cooking to allow the uncooked egg to flow under-neath. Cut frittata into wedges and serve immediately.

NOTE:
You can save any leftovers for a snack or a meal. Enjoy!

It is easier to build strong children than to repair broken men.

Frederick Douglass

> **DIETARY PRIORITIES**
> ① *Eliminating negative foods.*
> ② *Replace inferior foods.*
> ③ *Reduce excess.*

grains

A Different Kind of Delightful Pancake

Serves 2-3

1 CUP OF COTTAGE CHEESE OR
RICOTTA CHEESE

1 CUP OF APPLES, DICED

½ CUP OF STRAWBERRIES, SLICED

¾ CUP OF RICE FLOUR

½ TEASPOON OF STEVIA OR RAW HONEY

½ TEASPOON OF CINNAMON

½ TEASPOON OF NUTMEG

1 TEASPOON SUNFLOWER SEEDS

4 EGGS

DASH OF SEA SALT

BUTTER

Mix all the ingredients together in a large bowl. Mix until the batter is well blended. Heat butter in a large skillet and pour into pan. Let each side brown. You can serve with some fresh yogurt on the side. These pancakes are so delightful… they can even be used as a dessert.

Corn Meal Belly Warmer

Serves 2

2 CUPS OF COOKED CORN MEAL

2 CUPS OF RICE MILK OR
ORGANIC WHOLE MILK

¼ TEASPOON OF STEVIA OR
1 TEASPOON OF HONEY

2 EGGS

½ TEASPOON REAL VANILLA

1 TABLESPOON BUTTER

SPRINKLE WITH A FEW BERRIES

Combine the cooked corn meal, milk, berries and stevia or honey in a small saucepan. Bring to a boil and then reduce heat to low and simmer. After about 5 minutes, spoon out a bit of the hot mixture, and stir it into the bowl with the beaten eggs, slowly adding a tablespoon at a time until you have about ⅓ cup. Stir the egg/corn meal mixture back into the saucepan along with the vanilla and butter and continue cooking over low heat until thickened.

Corny Tortilla French Toast...Oui Oui

Serves 1-2

2 LARGE EGGS

1 TABLESPOON MILK

2 CORN TORTILLAS

8 BLUEBERRIES

BUTTER

CINNAMON

Use a bowl to whisk the eggs and milk together. Transfer to shallow dish. Place tortilla into egg mixture and let it soak up the egg batter. In a skillet, add 1 tablespoon of butter until the butter sizzles. Place the tortilla in a skillet adding any remaining batter to the corn tortilla. Flip the tortilla on each side until it is browned. Add in the blueberries. Roll up the tortilla and serve this hot. Sprinkle with cinnamon. This looks just like a crepe. Enjoy!

VARIATION:
Try this dish with a side of chicken sausage.

You could also mix in assorted berries.

Halloween Pumpkin Pancakes

Serves 1-2

⅓ CUP OF OATMEAL

⅓ CUP OF CANNED PUMPKIN

⅓ CUP COTTAGE CHEESE

3 EGGS

1 PACKET OF STEVIA (OPTIONAL)

OR 1 TEASPOON OF HONEY

1 TEASPOON VANILLA

DASH OF CINNAMON

1 TABLESPOON

(splash of water if too thick)

Mix ingredients together in a blender. Heat the pan and melt butter. Pour batter into a heated pan. Make sure the pancakes brown on each side. Serve hot! Enjoy!

FUN FACTS ABOUT PUMPKIN
Did you know that pumpkins contain potassium and Vitamin A and even have edible pumpkin flowers? The largest pumpkin pie ever made was over five feet in diameter and weighed over 350 pounds.

lunch & dinner

poultry

A Different Kind Of Roll Up—By Brian

Serves 2

1-4 SHEETS OF SPRING ROLL SKIN

(also known as rice paper)

ASSORTED STIR- FRIED VEGGIES

(such as bean sprouts, water chesnuts and bok choy)

CHICKEN, LAMB OR TURKEY, SHREDDED

ALMOND OR CASHEW SAUCE

(use real almond or cashew butter and thin it down with some water.)

For this recipe, make sure to involve your children. This is fun! Fill up a bowl of water for each child. Soak each sheet of rice paper in water for about 1-2 minutes. After you are done, place the sheet on a plate. Let the kids pile on the veggies and meat. Then roll up the rice paper and dip it in the almond or cashew sauce. This is Yummy!!!

VARIATION:
Add minced ginger and garlic for an adult taste.

Sweet & Sassy Shepard's Pie

Serves 4

6 SWEET POTATOES, PEELED AND QUARTERED

2 TURNIPS, PEELED AND CHOPPED

¼ CUP OF BUTTER

2 TABLESPOONS OF OLIVE OIL

1 ONION, MINCED

1½ CUPS OF NATURAL, ORGANIC TURKEY, GROUND

1 BAG OF ORGANIC FROZEN CORN
—feel free to add in other vegetables as well

1 BAG OF ORGANIC FROZEN PEAS

2 TABLESPOONS OF GARLIC POWDER

DASH OF SEA SALT

Cut the sweet potatoes and turnips in quarters and place in a saucepan. Add enough water to cover the ingredients. Then add a dash of salt. Bring the water to a boil over high heat. Lower the heat and continue to boil for about 30 minutes. Sauté the vegetables and onions. Crumble in the ground turkey and stir together until the meat is done. Simmer for about 5 minutes. Get back to the sweet potatoes and turnips, drain them. Add in the butter, salt and milk and mash the sweet potatoes. Put the meat and vegetables in a large size-baking pan and cover the meat with the potatoes and turnips. Dot the sweet potatoes and turnips with butter. Bake for about one hour until crusty and golden brown. Take out from the oven, and cool for about 10 minutes. Serve and enjoy!

Chicken Quesadillas Mi Amigo with Sweet Squash

Serves 2-3

1 TABLESPOON OF OLIVE OIL

½ POUND OF NATURAL CHICKEN THIGHS

½ TEASPOON OF SEA SALT

⅛ TEASPOON OF CHILI POWDER

½ CUP OF BUTTERNUT SQUASH, PURÉED

½ CUP OF CHEDDAR CHEESE, SHREDDED

4 CORN TORTILLAS

Preheat the oven to 400°F. Oil the baking pan. Take out a large skillet and set over medium heat. Add olive oil to coat the pan. Sprinkle the chicken with sea salt and chili powder. Cook for about 4-5 minutes per side. Reduce heat to low and cook covered for about 10 more minutes. Shred the chicken into small strips. Mix the butternut squash with the shredded cheddar cheese. Spread the chicken and cheese mixture over the tortillas and put the second tortilla on top like a sandwich. Place on the baking pan and bake until crisp for about 5 minutes, or until done. Cut into wedges and serve with salsa.

A WORD ON ZINC
Chicken, turkey, red meats, and eggs are good sources of zinc. Today there is almost a universal need for this important mineral because soils are low in zinc due to modern farming methods. Zinc is necessary for protein synthesis, carbohydrate metabolism, the nervous system and endocrine system—just to name a few of the many important functions that this mineral performs.

Brian's Tortilla Cigars

Serves 3-4

Great for a snack or lunch—these pack well.

2 CUPS OF ROASTED OR SAUTÉED NATURAL CHICKEN OR TURKEY, CUBED

½ CUP OF CHEDDAR CHEESE, SHREDDED

¼ TEASPOON OF GARLIC POWDER

¼ TEASPOON OF SEA SALT

6 LARGE CORN TORTILLAS

Preheat the oven to 350°F. Line the baking pan with parchment paper. Cut the tortillas in half. Spread about two tablespoons of the filing, (chicken, cheddar cheese, garlic powder and sea salt) along the center of the tortilla. Starting at the edge, roll the tortilla into a cigar shape, completely enclosing the filling. Place seam-side down on the baking sheet. Do the same for all the tortillas. Bake until the tortillas begin to brown. It takes about 4-5 minutes.

Great for snack or lunch—these pack well!

(simple) It's a Rainbow Tostada Sandwich

Serves 4

4 CORN TORTILLAS

1 CUP OF BLACK BEANS

1 CUP OF LETTUCE, SHREDDED

2 CUPS OF EGGS, CHOPPED OR
2 CUPS OF NATURAL CHICKEN, CHOPPED

1 CUP OF GRATED RAW MILK CHEESE
OF YOUR CHOICE

1 DAB OF SOUR CREAM

Using a fry pan, lightly sauté the tortillas in butter. You could also place the tortillas in the toaster oven at 350°F for about 5 minutes. They should get toasty and a bit brown. For best results, turn tortillas often, as they will burn. You can even make extra. Simply wrap them up in paper towels and put them on a plate for a snack later. When the tortillas are ready, call the kids over and get them involved in this fun meal. Place all your ingredients out on the table, and let the kids arrange their meal on their own plates. Enjoy!

DID YOU KNOW?

In the late 1800's most Americans ate three homecooked meals a day, made with whole foods. In the 1980's research showed that the great majority of Americans did not eat three family meals each day at home. Whole foods were not selected frequently. What does the new millennium say about meal time habits? No time to cook, little time to spend together and not enough whole foods on the table. With already busy schedules, parents feel they don't have time to cook dinner. Kentucky Fried Chicken reported that take-out food was used by more than a quarter (28 percent) of families for the evening meal once a week; 20 percent said they used carryout twice a week and 12 percent said three times a week. (http://nutrition.wsu.edu/ebet/background.html)

It is easier to build strong children than to repair broken men.

Frederick Douglass

grass-fed beef

Divine Spaghetti Pie

Serves 4 or more

3 OUNCES RICE PASTA SPAGHETTI

1 POUND NATURAL TURKEY, GROUND OR NATURAL SIRLOIN, GROUND

1 LARGE EGG

2 TABLESPOONS PARMESAN CHEESE, GRATED

2 GLOVES GARLIC, CHOPPED

2 CUPS TOMATO SAUCE

½ TEASPOON SALT

1 CUP MOZZARELLA, SHREDDED

Preheat oven to 350°F. Bring water to a boil in a large pot. Add in pasta, and cook until al dente. Drain pasta. In a small bowl, mix the ground turkey or ground beef with the egg, Parmesan cheese and garlic. Form the mixture into ½ inch balls.

In a large bowl, stir the cooked rice pasta, tomato sauce, and sea salt. Spoon the mixture into the pie plate and smooth the top. Scatter meatballs on top and sprinkle with mozzarella. Bake uncovered for about 25-30 minutes or until the center is firm and the cheese is bubbly.

NOTE:
This dish contains tomatoes, a member of the nightshade family that can aggravate inflammatory conditions.

Kid's Kaboodle's Steak Kabob's

Serves 4 or more

8 OUNCES OF BUTTON MUSHROOMS

1 MEDIUM ONION

1½ POUNDS OF NATURAL BEEF SIRLOIN, OR NATURAL LAMB

2 TABLESPOONS OF BALSAMIC VINEGAR

2 TABLESPOONS OLIVE OIL

1 TABLESPOON GARLIC, CHOPPED

SKEWERS

Wash mushrooms and remove dirt. Cut onion in quarters. Slice peppers lengthwise. Cut meat into 1 inch pieces and place in a bowl. Add the vinegar, oil and garlic and stir to combine. Cover the bowl tightly with plastic wrap and refrigerate for at least 2-4 hours. Preheat oven to 450°F or place on grill for about 5 minutes per side. Thread meat and vegetables on a skewer and place on baking sheet. Bake for about 10 minutes. Serve with brown rice.

NOTE:
This makes a great packable snack for the next day. Make extras for leftovers. Mothers in the Nutrition Education Network of Washington's focus groups said, "When we eat together, we eat better"

Eat 'Em Up! Sloppy Joe's

Serves 4 or more

1 TABLESPOON OF OLIVE OIL

½ CUP OF RED ONION, MINCED

½ CUP OF CELERY, MINCED

2 CLOVES GARLIC, MINCED

1 POUND OF NATURAL TURKEY, GROUND
OR GRASS-FED SIRLOIN, GROUND

½ CUP SWEET POTATO PURÉE

½ CARROTS RAW, FINELY CHOPPED

¼ CUP TOMATO PASTE

1 TEASPOON CHILI POWDER

½ TEASPOON SEA SALT

BLUE TACO SHELLS OR CORN TORTILLA

Coat a large skillet with olive oil and place over medium heat. Add in the onions, celery and garlic and cook until the onions soften. Add in the meat and cook for about 5 minutes until brown. Add all vegetable purées, raw carrots, tomato paste, chili powder, and sea salt. Reduce the heat to low, cover and simmer until half reduces liquid. Cook for 15 minutes. Serve in a taco shell or in a tortilla.

NOTE:
This dish contains tomatoes, a member of the nightshade family that can aggravate inflammatory conditions.

Mexican Nacho Hat Dance!

BLUE CORN CHIPS

½ CUP CHEDDAR CHEESE, SHREDDED

2 CUPS OF NATURAL CHICKEN OR
NATURAL LAMB, GROUND
COOKED AND SHREDDED

SALSA

Cover a plate with blue corn chips. Sprinkle on shredded cheddar cheese. Feel free to add on shredded chicken or ground beef and beans. Bake in the oven for 5-10 minutes at 350°F. Then, garnish with shredded lettuce and steamed veggies. You can serve with a side of salsa.

VARIATION:
Try shredding an array of different vegetables and mixing them into the meat to give children as much nutrients as possible.

NOTE:
This dish contains tomatoes, a member of the nightshade family that can aggravate inflammatory conditions.

Mighty Healthy Meatloaf

Serves 4 or more

1 CUP OF GLUTEN-FREE BREADCRUMBS
OR RICE CEREAL

½ CUP OF WHOLE MILK

3 TABLESPOONS OF OLIVE OIL

½ CUP OF ONIONS, PURÉED

½ CUP OF CARROTS, PURÉED

½ CUP OF CELERY, PURÉED

1 POUND OF NATURAL TURKEY, GROUND
OR GRASS-FED BEEF, GROUND

½ CUP OF PARMESAN CHEESE

2 EGGS

1 TEASPOON OF SEA SALT

Preheat the oven to 350°F. Coat the pan with a dab of olive oil. In a bowl, mix the breadcrumbs and the milk and let it soak. Mix together the meat, tomato sauce and eggs, and Parmesan cheese. Add in gluten-free breadcrumbs and the puréed vegetables. Stir until combined. Put the meatloaf mixture onto an oiled baking pan and then shape. Bake for about 45-50 minutes or until the meatloaf is no longer pink on the inside.

NOTE:
This recipe makes great leftovers for the next day!

Children are one third of our population and all of our future.

Select Panel for the Promotion of Child Health, 1981

DID YOU KNOW?
In a Harvard study children who ate family dinners most days consumed more fruits and vegetables and less fried foods, saturated fats, trans-fats and soda than children who never or hardly ate dinner with family members Children who ate dinners with family members most days had substantially higher intakes of dietary fiber, calcium, iron, folate, vitamins B-6, B-12, C and E.

Lamb

(simple) Middle Eastern Lamb Kebob

Serves 4

1 POUND OF NATURAL LAMB, GROUND

1 TEASPOON OF PLAIN YOGURT

1 ONION, MINCED

1 TEASPOON OF CURRY POWDER

DASH OF SEA SALT

Mix all the ingredients together well. Divide into 4 portions. Use your hands to shape the mixture into a long log and pat around the skewer. Cook over a hot grill for about 7-10 minutes while rotating the skewers every few minutes.

Sami's Kicking n' Rocking' American Chop Suey

Serves 4 or more

1 POUND OF NATURAL TURKEY OR NATURAL LAMB, GROUND

1 BOX OF RICE PASTA

1 CHOPPED ONION

1 CUP OF VEGETABLES, PURÉED
(puréed cauliflower works well—try zucchini also)

2 CLOVES OF GARLIC, MINCED

¼ CUP OF PARMESAN CHEESE, FRESHLY GRATED

12 OUNCES OF TOMATO SAUCE

2 TEASPOONS CHILI POWDER

DASH OF SEA SALT

OLIVE OIL

Cook the rice pasta according to the package directions. Sauté the onions and garlic in a small amount of olive oil then add the meat and cook over medium-high heat until done. Preheat oven to 350°F. Drain the grease from the pan, and then add sea salt to taste. In a large saucepan, combine the sauce, the ¼ cup of cheese, and the beef or turkey mixture and bring to a simmer. Add the pasta, turn off the heat, and let it set for 5 minutes. Pour the ingredients into a large baking pan and bake in the oven for about 10 minutes. Finally, garnish individual portions with lots of grated Parmesan cheese.

NOTE:
This dish contains tomatoes, a member of the nightshade family that can aggravate inflammatory conditions.

Sprinkled Lamb Patties

Serves 4

1 POUND OF NATURAL LAMB, GROUND

1 ZUCCHINI, SHREDDED

SEA SALT

Mix the lamb with the shredded zucchini. Shape into patties. Place in the broiler for about 7 minutes per side.

VARIATION:
You can also cook these patties in a sauce-pan. Cover bottom of the pan with ¼ inch of water and simmer each side for 7 minutes.

(simple) Mary Had a Little Lamb Chop

Serves 2

4 SMALL NATURAL LAMB CHOPS

SEA SALT

1 TABLESPOON OF ROSEMARY

Turn the oven on to broil. Place lamb chops on a broiling pan. Sprinkle on sea salt and rosemary. Broil for about 7 minutes per side.

MYTH
A lowfat diet is beneficial to children.

TRUTH
Children on lowfat diets suffer from growth problems, failure to thrive and learning disabilities.(Food Chem News 1994)

Twisted Blue Tacos

Serves 4 or more

1 TABLESPOON OF OLIVE OIL

1 POUND OF NATURAL LAMB OR TURKEY, GROUND

½ CUP OF SWEET POTATO PURÉE

½ PACKET OF NATURAL TACO SEASONING

1 PACKAGE OF BLUE TACO SHELLS

½ CUP MOZZARELLA OR CHEDDAR CHEESE, SHREDDED

TOPPINGS:

½ CUP OF FROZEN CORN KERNELS

3 LARGE LEAVES OF LEAFY LETTUCE, SLICED THINLY

Coat a skillet with olive oil and set over medium heat. Add the meat and stir with a large wood spoon for about 4-5 minutes. Put in vegetable purée and seasoning mix. Reduce the heat to low and simmer until the meat is no longer pink. Preheat the oven to 325°F and fill the taco shells with the meat mixture and sprinkle with cheese. Cook for about 5 minutes. Add your favorite toppings.

vegetables

Ava's Vegetastic Pizza Pie

Serves 4

GLUTEN-FREE CRUST

4 CUPS SPINACH STEAMED AND PUT IN
THE FOOD PROCESSOR

2 CUPS ORGANIC TOMATO SAUCE OR
PESTO SAUCE

RAW CHEDDAR CHEESE-SHREDDED,
AS NEEDED

OPTIONAL:

natural hot dogs, minced

turkey bacon, minced

onions, chopped

olives

Prepare gluten free crust according to directions. After crust is cooked, take crust out of oven and brush with olive oil. Mix spinach and tomato or pesto sauce together and pour onto crust and spread evenly. Add shredded cheese. Feel free to add meat, olives, chopped onions. Put back in oven for 10-15 minutes on 450°F.

Ava loves this and if she gives it the thumbs up! Go ahead, give this recipe a try.

Bugs Bunny's Favorite Carrot Soup

Serves 6

2 MEDIUM ONIONS,
PEELED AND CHOPPED

1 POUND OF CARROTS, PEELED AND SLICED

4 TABLESPOONS BUTTER

2 TEASPOONS CURRY POWDER

1½ QUARTS OF CHICKEN BROTH OR WATER

½ TEASPOON OF GRATED GINGER

Sauté onions and carrots very gently in butter about 45 minutes. Add curry powder and stir around until well mixed. Add broth or water, bring to a boil and skim. Add ginger. Simmer, covered about 15 minutes. Purée soup and season to taste. You can even add a dollop of raw cream to the top.

Sprinkles on Rice

Serves 4

1 CUP OF COOKED BROWN RICE

1 CUP OF CARROTS OR ZUCCHINI, SHREDDED

PINCH OF SEA SALT

Place 1 cup of brown rice into 2 cups of water. Bring rice to a boil and then simmer for 40-60 minutes in a covered pot. Toss vegetables (The sprinkles) into the pot where the rice is cooking. This is approximately 20 minutes before the rice is completed. Add a pinch of sea salt.

Tell your children how healthy and beautiful they look after eating such wonderful foods.

NOTE:
Please feel free to rotate in a variety of shredded vegetables.

Grill It Sweet Cheese Sandwich

Serves 1

½ CUP OF RAW CHEDDAR CHEESE, SHREDDED

½ CUP OF SWEET POTATO OR BUTTERNUT SQUASH PURÉE

2 SLICES OF RICE BREAD OR SPROUTED GRAINS BREAD

BUTTER

SEA SALT

In a bowl, mix the cheese, purée and a pinch of sea salt together. On two slices of bread spread the cheese mixture. Cover sandwich. Melt butter in a pan and place a pat of butter on each side of the bread. When the skillet is hot, put the sandwich on the skillet, on medium heat. Gently brown for about 4 minutes per side.

 # Are these Fries? They're Carrots

Makes 4 servings

4 LARGE CARROTS

1 TABLESPOON OF BUTTER

½ TEASPOON OF SALT

Preheat your oven to 425°F. Cut off the tips of the carrots and peel. Then cut the carrot in half and slice lengthwise. Repeat this with the remaining carrots. In a separate bowl, melt the butter. Add in sea salt and stir. Coat the carrots with the butter, and salt mixture. Place the carrots on a baking pan. Bake until the carrots are tender, or for about 15 minutes. They are delicious hot!

(simple) Cobby Corn

Serves 4

4 EARS OF CORN

½ OF A STICK OF BUTTER

PINCH OF SEA SALT

Snap the corn in half. Place an ear of corn standing upright on your counter. Using a knife cut the corn off the cob. Turn the cob so that all of the corn is removed. Continue and repeat with the remaining corn. Heat up your skillet and melt your butter. Stir in your corn kernels, salt and toss for 3-5 minutes. The corn should be crispy and crunchy. I would recommend serving this immediately. You can even sprinkle on some Parmesan cheese if you would like.

Make 'em Happy with Sweet Potato Oven Crisps

Serves 8

EXTRA VIRGIN OLIVE OIL

2 POUNDS OF SWEET POTATOES, SKIN ON, SCRUBBED AND THINLY SLICED

½ TEASPOON SEA SALT

Preheat oven to 450°F. Lightly coat baking pan with olive oil. Arrange the sweet potato slices in a row, making sure they do not overlap. Season with sea salt. Bake for 15-20 minutes, until crispy and golden brown.

NOTE:
Slice potatoes as thinly as possible so that they get crispy. To make this fun, try taking different colored paper/plastic cups and lining them with festive paper towels. Stack the sweet potato crisps in the cup and watch your kids devour these nutritious crisps.

(simple) Megan's Twist on Macaroni and Cheese

Serves 4

2 CUPS OF BROWN RICE

1 CUP OF COOKED PEAS

⅓ CUP OF PARMESAN CHEESE
(try sheep's milk or raw milk cheese)

Place 1 cup of brown rice in 2 cups of water. Bring to a boil and then simmer for 40-60 minutes in a covered pot. Add in peas about 10 minutes before rice is done cooking. Sprinkle in the Parmesan cheese. Mix all ingredients together.

NOTE:
You can add shredded chicken for additional protein.

 Yummy Tummy Salads

LETTUCE

Choose from Romaine, Bibb, Red Leaf, Green Leaf, Watercress, Mesculin, Arugula and Endive.

ACCOMPANIMENTS:

CARROT STICKS
SLICED CELERY
CUCUMBER
SHREDDED ZUCCHINI
SUNFLOWER SEEDS
GOAT CHEESE

Steam up broccoli, cauliflower, and asparagus

One of the tricks I learned over the years of raising kids is to always get them involved in what I am preparing and cooking. When children feel a part of the process, they are more likely to try new foods. I often let them thumb through the cookbook recipes and have them pick out what they like. In this recipe I have provided you with some ideas for salads.

Although this is a basic salad recipe, you can add in all different types of accompaniments.

I would let the kids make all the decisions as to what type of lettuce they like, vegetables, and dressings.

Pleasurable Puréed Parsnips

Serves 4

4 CUPS OF PARSNIPS

OPTIONAL:
2 cups of carrots
4 tablespoons of butter
¼ cup of heavy cream
A pinch of sea salt

Peel parsnips and chop them up. Put parsnips into a pot of boiling water.

OPTIONAL: add in carrots at this point if you would like to include them in the recipe

Let them boil for about 10 minutes or until tender. Drain out water and put parsnips into a food processor. Add cream and add salt.

This is a sweet and delicious dish.

DID YOU KNOW?
Researchers in Norway surveyed 54,000 people and found that a sense of humor can extend life for those who are sick. Those that had cancer and a sense of humor were 70 percent more likely to survive than their counterparts with little or no sense of humor.

Side Saddle of Carrots

Serves 2

2 CARROTS

HEALTHY MAYONNAISE

½ CUP OF RAISINS

½ CUP OF WALNUTS, CHOPPED

LEMON JUICE

Peel carrots. Then use a grater to shred the carrots. Mix the shredded carrots with the raisins, lemon juice, mayonnaise and chopped walnuts.

Serve and eat.

JUNK FOOD

Junk food makes people insane! The increase in mental disorders in the last several years could be attributed to the increase in the consumption of an unhealthy diet. People eat ⅓ less vegetables than they did 50 years ago (BBC News)

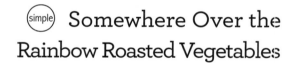 # Somewhere Over the Rainbow Roasted Vegetables

Serves 4

¼ CUP OF CARROTS

¼ CUP OF BRUSSELS SPROUTS

¼ CUP OF GOLDEN BEETS

BUTTER

SEA SALT

Preheat oven to 350°F. Then place the assorted vegetables on a roasting pan. Drizzle with melted butter and sea salt. Roast in the oven for about 20 minutes. When the vegetables are roasted, remove from the oven and let them cool. Have your children arrange them in a rainbow design on their plates.

This is a fun recipe for the children to participate in!

(simple) Steamin' Demon Veggies

Serves 4

1 CUP OF BROCCOLI, CHOPPED

1 CUP OF CAULIFLOWER, CHOPPED

1 CUP OF ZUCCHINI, SLICED

1 CUP OF CARROTS, SLICED

¼ CUP OF ALMOND BUTTER

Place vegetables in a steamer basket for 5 minutes. Remove vegetables from basket and place them into a new bowl. In a separate bowl, mix the almond butter with a few tablespoons of water to thin down this sauce. Pour the almond butter over the vegetables.

The children will just love this dish.

Broccoli is a nutritional powerhouse as it is loaded with vitamins and minerals such as, C, B complex, calcium, phosphorus, and chromium. It is also rich in indoles, a potent anticancer property.

A WORD ON BEETS

Long valued as a blood tonic, beets are rich in calcium, iron, magnesium and phosphorus as well as carotene, B complex and vitamin C. The greens have the bonus of carotenoids. Always buy beets with their greens (they are delicious cooked with butter and garlic) as they are an excellent indication of freshness. The combination is excellent both nutritionally and taste wise.

(simple) Cinnamon Carrots

Serves 1-2

2 LARGE CARROTS

1 TABLESPOON BUTTER

1 TEASPOON CINNAMON

Peel and clean carrots. Cut carrots into 2 inch slices. Place carrots in the steamer basket for about 5 minutes. Dot with butter and sprinkle on the cinnamon.

NOTE:
Try to purchase the carrots with green tops. They are sweeter and more nutritious.

Spaghetti—Is it Really a Vegetable Mom?

Serves 4

1 WHOLE SPAGHETTI SQUASH

⅓ CUP OF HEAVY CREAM

½ STICK OF BUTTER

½ CUP OF APPLE CHUNKS

In a very large pot, bring water to a boil. When the water is boiling, drop the whole squash in the pot. Cook for about 30 minutes. When a fork slides easily into the squash, it is fully cooked. Remove the squash from the water and wait for it to cool. Then split the squash in half length-wise and remove the seeds and the stringy portion. Now, get the kids over for this part. It is fun. With a fork, comb the squash and you will see the spaghetti pull off in strands. Now use a large skillet on medium heat and melt the butter in the pan. Sauté the squash add the heavy cream and the chopped apple. Cook for about 5-10 minutes. Enjoy!

OPTION:
You could also prepare the squash with a dollop of melted butter on top. This is a quick and easy alternative.

Crystal's Surprise Brownies

Serves 6-8

1 CUP RICE FLOUR

1 TEASPOON OF SEA SALT

1 TEASPOON BAKING POWDER

1 CUP WHOLE MILK

2 EGGS

1 HALF CUP BUTTER

1 HALF ONION, FINELY CHOPPED

1 CUP SHARP CHEDDAR CHEESE, SHREDDED

10 OUNCES OF SPINACH, UNCOOKED

Sauté the onions and spinach in butter. Mix all other ingredients together. Transfer spinach into mixed ingredients. Pour into greased 9x13 inch pan. Cook for 30-35 minutes at 350°F. Surprise!

SAMPLE MENUS

For those who cannot decide among all of these tasty choices,
here are some of my favorite meals:

BREAKFAST

Brown Rice Belly Warmer *(See page 135)*
Cup of Herbal Tea or Hot Water with lemon

Mexican Scrambled Eggs *(See page 129)*
Cup of Herbal Tea or Hot Water and lemon

Delightful Oatmeal Pancakes *(See page 135)*
Cup of Herbal Tea or Hot Water and lemon

LUNCH

Easy Roll–Ups Smoked Salmon and Goat Cheese *(See page 149)*
Tossed Salad with the Best Salad Dressing *(See page 195)*

Broiled Lamb Chops *(See page 152)*
½ Plate of Broccoli Rabe with Garlic *(See page 168)*
Carousel Turkey Surprise *(See page 141)*
Jazzy Green Beans and Garlic *(See page 174)*
A Mixed Salad with The Best Salad Dressing *(See page 195)*

DINNER

Minty Lamb with Lemon *(See page 153)*
Fried Rice Plus Vegetables *(See page 185)*
Argula with The Best Salad Dressing *(See page 195)*

Apple of My Eye Brisket *(See page 156)*
Sweeties Potato Oven Crisps *(See page 214)*
Cauliflower au Gratin *(See page 172)*

Broiled Salmon *(See page 148)*
Roasted Asparagus *(See page 175)*
Mix N' Match Quinoa *(See page 183)*
Mixed Salad with The Best Salad Dressing *(See page 195)*

TEAR ALONG EDGE HERE

SHOPPING LIST OF FOODS - THE ESSENTIALS OF GOOD HEALTH

SPICES
- Basil
- Cayenne
- Cilantro
- Cinnamon
- Coriander
- Cumin
- Curry
- Dill
- Dulse
- Garlic
- Ginger
- Kelp
- Lemongrass
- Oregano
- Paprika
- Poppy seeds
- Rosemary
- Saffron
- Sea salt
- Tarragon
- Thyme
- Turmeric

OILS & BUTTERS
- Butter
- Coconut oil - optional
- Olive oil
- Flax oil
- Hemp oil

NUTS & NUT BUTTERS
- Almond butter
- Cashew butter
- Sunflower butter

VINEGAR & OTHER CONDIMENTS
- Balsamic vinegar
- Cider vinegar
- Healthy mayonaise
- Mustard
- Rice vinegar
- Sea salt
- San-J® Organic, Tamari soy sauce

PODS & SEEDS
- Corn
- Green beans
- Peas

SEA VEGETABLES
- Kombu

ONION FAMILY
- Garlic
- Leeks
- Onions

ROOT VEGETABLES
- Beets
- Carrots
- Celery root
- Parsnips
- Radishes
- Rutabagas
- Sweet potatoes
- Turnips

BRASSICAS & GREEN LEAFY VEGETABLES
- Broccoli
- Brussel sprouts
- Cabbage
- Cauliflower
- Collard greens
- Spinach
- Swiss chard

PUMPKINS & SQUASH
- Butternut
- Pumpkin
- Squash
- Summer squashes
- Winter squashes
- Zucchini

SHOOT VEGETABLES
- Artichokes
- Asparagus
- Celery
- Endive
- Fennel

SPROUTED SEEDS
- Adzuki bean sprouts
- Alfalfa sprouts
- Garbanzo
- Bean sprouts
- Lentil sprouts
- Mung bean sprouts
- Wheat berry sprouts

PROTEINS
- Grass fed beef
- Natural chicken and turkey sausage
- Natural and organic Chicken and turkey
- Natural turkey bacon
- Natural lamb
- Salmon
- Sardines

DAIRY
- Cream
- Crème fraiche
- Eggs
- Goat cheese
- Goat milk
- Organic milk
- Plain yogurt
- Raw cheese
- Sheep milk cheese
- Sour cream

GRAINS/BEANS
- Beans
- Blue & yellow taco shells
- Blue corn chips
- Brown rice pasta
- Brown rice
- Buckwheat
- Corn meal
- Corn tortillas
- Lentils
- Millet
- Peas
- Quinoa
- Wheat free-sugar free cereals

BEVERAGES
- Almond milk-unsweetened
- Assorted herbal teas chamomile, raspberry, peach, strawberry, green teas
- Distilled water
- Goat milk
- Organic milk
- Rice milk-unsweetened
- Sparkling water

COOKWARE
- Crock-pot
- Electric steamer
- Excellent knives for cutting vegetables
- Glass cookware/stainless steel pots
- Magic Bullet™ mini food processor
- Measuring cups and spoons
- Pressure cooker
- Slotted spoons
- Small sized ramekins ceramic or glass–serving bowl used for the preparation and serving of various food dishes.
- Timer

STORAGE CONTAINERS
- Freezer storage containers
- Glass storage containers
- Zip top storage bags–all sizes

FRUITS
- Apples
- Blueberries
- Lemons
- Limes
- Raspberries
- Strawberries

SWEETENERS
- Raw Honey
- Agave
- Stevia
- Pure Maple Syrup

Organic and natural produce, meats and oils are best!

APPENDICES

Everything You May Want to Know About Hair Analysis

Hair tissue mineral analysis is a way to assess the stress response in a human being, as well as to assist in designing an individualized nutritional balancing program. The test screens for twenty minerals and toxic metals in a sample of hair. Hair, like all other body tissues, contains minerals that are deposited as the hair grows. Although the hair is dead, the minerals remain as the hair continues to grow out. A sample of hair cut close to the scalp provides information about the mineral activity in the hair that took place over the past three to four months, depending on the rate of hair growth.

FROM HAIR, YOU CAN LEARN THE FOLLOWING:

1. Information about your metabolic rate

2. Stage of stress

3. Immune system

4. Adrenal and thyroid activity all on a cellular level

5. Knowledge regarding your bodies carbohydrate tolerance

6. Facts about your energy levels

7. Trends for over 30 illnesses

8. Information about personality tendencies, how you handle stress and your stress level.

WHAT IS HAIR MINERAL ANALYSIS?

Hair analysis is a soft tissue mineral biopsy. A biopsy is an analysis of a body tissue, in this case, to detect mineral levels and toxic metal levels. Hair is classified as a soft tissue of the body. It provides a reading of the mineral deposition in the cells and interstitial spaces of the hair.

WHY USE HAIR?

Hair makes an excellent biopsy material for a variety of reasons:

1. Sampling is simple and non-invasive.

2. Hair is a stable biopsy material. It requires no special handling and will remain viable for years.

3. Mineral levels in the hair are about ten times that of the blood, making them easy to detect in the hair.

4. Advancements in technology have rendered hair mineral analysis cost effective, accurate and reliable.

REASONS FOR USING HAIR IN THE DETECTION OF NUTRITIONAL AND BIOCHEMICAL IMBALANCES ARE AS FOLLOWS:

Hair provides a unique cellular reading of the mineral levels. The cells, not the blood or urine, are the major site of metabolic activity. Blood tests are excellent, but do not provide the same information for the following reasons:

- *MINERAL LEVELS ARE LOWER IN THE BLOOD, MAKING DETECTION OF TRACE ELEMENTS MORE DIFFICULT*

- *MINERAL LEVELS ARE KEPT CONSTANT IN THE BLOOD*

- *TOXIC METALS ARE NOT FOUND IN HIGH CONCENTRATIONS IN THE BLOOD EXCEPT AFTER ACUTE EXPOSURE*

- *BLOOD TESTS CAN VARY FROM HOUR TO HOUR DEPENDING ON DIET, TIME OF DAY AND MANY OTHER FACTORS.*

- *HAIR ANALYSIS IS ACKNOWLEDGED TO BE ONE OF THE FEW WAYS TO DETECT TOXIC METALS.*

WHERE DOES THE HAIR GET SENT?

Analytical Research Labs (ARL) is one of the most respected and experienced leaders in hair tissue mineral analysis. ARL has been setting professional standards that have been emulated for decades by national and international hair testing and interpretation laboratories. ARL, which pioneered the field of hair tissue mineral analysis interpretation, has earned the respect and endorsement of the health care professionals throughout the United States, Canada, Mexico, Europe and Asia. For more information about ARL, please visit their website at www.arltma.com

If you are interested in learning more about hair tissue mineral analysis you can contact Joy Feldman at www.joyfeldman.com or at joy@joyfeldman.com. Dr. Larry Wilson also has a wonderful website www.drlwilson.com, filled with hundreds of free articles on hair tissue mineral analysis and much more.

The Basic Modalities of Nutritional Balancing

Nutritional balancing includes the following modalities:

LIFESTYLE

This is the single most important physical element of this program. If the lifestyle is not healthful, the body will break down no matter how good the remedies, therapies or other healing methods. The main elements of lifestyle include, lots of rest and sleep. Balance in lifestyle is crucial.

DIET

A. How to obtain the most nutrients from an extremely nutrient depleted food supply,

B. How to avoid toxic chemical additives, pesticide residues that are in most food. The basic dietary principles have been outlined in this book.

DRINKING WATER

Water is critical to one's health. The main issues are cleanliness and ability to hydrate the body. Additional issues regarding water are outlined in this book.

NUTRITIONAL SUPPLEMENTS

These are needed today to help offset a depleted and toxic food supply, improper diets and eating habits, and often weak digestion that impairs nutrient absorption. Also food supplements can be used to enhance the stress response and balance body chemistry in very specific ways.

They can also help remove all toxic metals easily, quickly, deeply and without the need for chelating agents and other less safe methods. Food supplements are an absolute necessity today for almost everyone. In nutritional balancing science, all supplements are chosen carefully based mainly upon a properly performed hair analysis that is interpreted according to Dr. Eck's method.

INFRARED SAUNA THERAPY AND COLON CLEANSING

These procedures have been added to Dr. Eck's work by Dr. Larry Wilson. Reports from clients suggest that they add an entirely new potency and dimension to Dr. Eck's brilliant work.

THE ROY MASTERS OBSERVATION EXERCISE

This is another addition to Dr. Eck's work by Dr. Larry Wilson. This technique assists in balancing the body and teaches discipline that heals the body at deep levels if one practices this for an extended time.

APPENDIX C

Toxic Metals

According to Dr. Henry Schroeder, M.D., a leading authority on minerals states, "most organic substances are degradable by natural processes. However, no metal is degradable, they are here to stay for a long time."

Today most people have high levels of toxic metals. Sadly, individuals have the highest levels of toxic metals in history, several thousands times higher than a few hundred years ago. This is due to industrialization. According to Dr. Lawrence Wilson, author of *Nutritional Balancing Science (2010)*, toxic metals are a major cause of inflammation, infection, irritation and tissue damage.

Toxic metals replace nutrient minerals in the enzyme binding site, impacting the activity of the affected enzyme. An affected enzyme may only operate at 5-10 percent of its normal activity, or it may function at twice the normal rate. The damage due to environmental toxins are exacerbated by the reduced mineral content of and the contamination of the food supply. This is important to understand as the abundance of minerals in the diet protects the body against toxic metals. This is significant because minerals are necessary to enzyme functions and if the preferred minerals are not available in the food, the body picks up whatever minerals it can from the food, air and water as substitutes.

- *Replaces other minerals in tissue structures, such as the arteries, joints, which are weakened and/or destroyed by the replacement process.*

- *Supports fungal, bacterial and viral infections that are difficult to eliminate.*

LEAD

- Leaded gasoline
- Manufacture of batteries
- Cigarette smoke
- Drinking water
- "Grecian formula"
- Lead based paint
- Colored ink
- Pesticide residue
- Lead water pipes
- Children can be born with elevated lead, passed through the placenta. Diets deficient in calcium, magnesium or iron increase lead absorption.

MERCURY

- Dental Amalgams
- Tuna and Swordfish
- Contaminated drinking water
- Medications
  ex. Diuretics, mercurochrome, metholiate, contact lens solution
- Occupational exposure algicides, floor waxes, fabric softener
- Chemistry sets and old themometers
- All children are born with some mercury toxicity that is passed through the plecenta from their mothers.
- Mercury can also be passed to children in breast milk.

SYMPTOMS OF TOXICITY	EFFECTS ON HEALTH	SOLUTIONS
• **Musculo-skeletal system**: arthritis, osteo and rheumatoid, gout, low back pain, rickets • **Nervous system:** brain function, abnormal, blindness, convulsions deafness, dyslexia, encephalitis, epilepsy, fatigue, insomnia, MS, Parkinson's, vertigo • **Cardiovascular:** arteriosclerosis, artherosclerosis • **Digestive system:** abdominal pain, colic, constipation, indigestion, liver dysfunction, weight loss • **Hematological system:** anemia • **Reproductive system:** abortions, impotency, infertility, decreased libido, menstrual difficulties, sterility	• **Blood:** inhibits enzymes associated with hemoglobin synthesis, and increases the rate of destruction of red blood cells. End result is fatigue. • **Bones:** lead is incorporated into bone in preference to calcium. • **Brain:** can inhibit copper-dependent enzymes needed for neurotransmitters (dopamine, epinephrine, norepinephrine). • **Energy:** inhibits copper and iron-dependent enzymes in the Krebs cycle required for energy production. End result is fatigue. • **Kidneys:** lead can raise uric acid levels and impair kidney function. End result is gout. • **Minerals:** displaces and can cause deficiency or bio-unavailability of calcium, zinc, maganese, copper and iron.	• Stay away from poor quality drinking water, and cigarettes.
• **Adrenal gland dysfunction** • **Alopecia** • **Anorexia** • **Ataxia** • **Birth defects** • **Bruising** • **Brain damage** • **Depression** • **Dermatitis** • **Dizziness** • **Fatigue** • **Hyperactivity** • **Immune system dysfunction** • **Insomnia** • **Kidney damage** • **Loss of self-control** • **Memory loss** • **Mood swings** • **Migraine headaches** • **Nervousness, mood swings** • **Numbness and tingling in arms and legs** • **Pain in limbs** • **Rashes, skin**	• **Energy:** mercury compounds inhibit the enzyme ATPase, which impairs energy production in all body cells • **Nervous System:** degeneration of nerve fibers occurs particularly the peripheral sensory nerve fibers. In addition to sensory nerve damage motor conduction speed was reduced in persons with high mercury. In addition, parasthesia, pain in limbs, visual and audiory disturbances. Motor disturbances results in changes in gait, weakness, falling slurred speech and tremor. • **Headaches, rashes and emotional disturbances** • **Endocrine:** Concentrates in the thyroid and pituitary gland interfering with their function. • **Kidneys:** accumulate and can cause damage • **Psychological:** severe emotional difficulties including, ADD, ADHD, Autism and some Schizoid.	• Stay away from large fish-such as swordfish, tuna, shark and tile fish. Eat sardines, and salmon one time a month.

	SOURCE	SYMPTOMS OF TOXICITY	
CADMIUM	• Food grown on cadmium–contained soil, sewage. • Large ocean fish: tuna, cod and haddock. • Refined and processed foods • Cigarette smoke • Contaminated drinking water • Motor oil • Air pollution	• Alopecia, anemia • Atherosclerosis • Ateriosclerosis • Arthritis, Osteo • Arthritis, Rheumatoid • Bone repair, inhibited • Cancer • Cardiovascular disease • Cholesterol, elevated • Cirrhosis of the liver • Diabetes	• Enlarged heart • Failure to thrive syndrome • Fertility, decreased • Hyperactivity • Hypoglycemia • Inflammation • Migraine headaches • Renal disease • Schizophrenia • Low sex drive
ARSENIC	• Pesticides, beer, table salt, drinking water, paints pigments, cosmetics, rat poison, glass and mirror manufacture, fungicides and wood preservatives	• Enzyme inhibitor • Anorexia • Weakness • Diarrhea • Edema • Impaired healing • Dermatitis • Liver dysfunction	• Hair loss • Headaches • Muscle spasm • Jaundice, herpes, abnormal ECG, intereferes with the uptake of folic acid.
ALUMINUM	• Beverages from aluminum cans • Food cooked in aluminum cookware • Use of anti-perspirants • Drinking water • Drying agents in salt	• Early symptoms include: flatulence, headaches, colic, dryness of skin and mucous membranes, tendency for colds, burning in the head relieved by food, heartburn and an aversion to meat	• Later symptoms may include: Alzheimers, ALS, Anemia, Colitis, Dental cavities, Parkinson's disease
NICKEL	• Hydrogenated vegetable oil • Margarine • Imitation whip creams • Commercial peanut butter • Vegetarian products • Kelp • Unrefined grains • Oysters • Tea herring • Nickel plating • Manufacture of steel • Batteries, machine parts • Wire, electrical parts	• Kidney dysfunction • Heart attack • Cancer, oral • Cancer, intestinal • Skin problems • Nausea, vomiting	• Hemorrhages • Malaise • Low blood pressure • Muscle tremors, tetany and paralysis

EFFECTS ON HEALTH	SOLUTIONS
• **Cancer:** very toxic metal usually accosiated with the development of cancer. • **Energy:** Causes strong inhibition of essential enzymes in the Krebs Cycle. • **Nervous System:** cadmium inhibits release of acetylcholine and activates cholinesterase. Results in a tendency for hyperactivity of the nervous system. Cadmium also directly damages nerve cells. • **Bones and Joints:** alters calcium and phosphorus metabolism, contributing to arthritis, osteoporosis and neuromuscular diseases. • **Cardiovascular system:** replaces zinc in the arteries contributing to brittle, inflexible arteries. • **Digestive system:** intereferes with production of digestive enzymes that require zinc.	• **Stay away from large fish, avoid processed meats, colas and contaminated drinking water.**
• **Irritation of the stomach and intestines, decreased production of red and white blood cells, skin changes and lung irritation.** It is suggested that the uptake of significant amounts of inorganic arsenic can intensify the chances of cancer development, especially the chances of development of skin cancer, lung cancer, liver cancer and lymphatic cancer. • **A very high exposure to inorganic arsenic can cause infertility and miscarriages with women, and it can cause skin disturbances, declined resistance to infections, heart disruptions and brain damage with both men and women.** • **Can damage DNA.**	• **Eat organic food.** • **Avoid most fish, large fish, and shell fish.**
• **Nervous System:** In animal studies, aluminum blocks the electrical discharge of nerve cells, reducing nervous system activity. It also inhibits enzymes in the brain (NA-K-ATPase and hexokinase). • **It may also inhibit uptake of important chemicals by nerve cells** • **Behavorial effects:** Dementia can result from kidney dialysis related to aluminum toxicity. It can cause memory loss of coordination, confusion and disorienation. • **Digestive system:** Aluminum reduces intestinal activity. An excess may cause colic.	• **Use Sea Salt and remove processed foods and canned drinks from diet. Use aluminum free deodorant and buy stainless steel cookware.**
• **Kidneys:** nickel has a tendency to accumulate in the kidneys • **Hormone, lipid and membrane metabolism:** it is believed that nickel has some physiological role related to these functions	• **Remove hydrogenated foods from diet as well as fast foods.**

* Hair levels of toxic metals may rise over time on a nutrition program as more toxic metals are mobilized from tissue storage sites.

The Major Vitamins and Minerals

VITAMIN A

Vitamin A is a fat-soluble vitamin discovered in 1906. It is one of the most important, and is often deficient in young people today, especially vegetarians or those who do not eat much meat. Vitamin A can tend to slow the oxidation or metabolic rate.

FOOD SOURCES

The best sources are meats such as liver, chicken, turkey and fish oils. Vegetables do not contain preformed Vitamin A. Instead, some colored vegetables contain beta-carotene, which can be converted to Vitamin A in the body. However, if the thyroid gland is sluggish, and this is very common, the body often cannot convert carotenes to fully formed Vitamin A. Therefore, we never depend upon beta-carotene or other carotenes in vegetables as good sources of Vitamin A.

FUNCTIONS

One of its major roles is to strengthen and support epithelial cells, which make up the skin and mucus membranes of the body. Mucus membranes are exactly like skin, but are inside the body such as the lining of your mouth, throat, digestive tract and elsewhere.

Vitamin A thus strengthens the body's ability to keep out all invading bacteria and other pathogenic or disease-causing micro-organisms. For this reason, Vitamin A assists the immune response of the body. One can take more Vitamin A if one feels one is getting a cold, for example, and it will often help stop the cold altogether or reduce its duration and severity.

Vitamin A is also needed in the retina for vision, blood formation, genetic activity such as protein synthesis, proper growth and development, an anti-oxidant, and bone formation. In high doses, it may be helpful for some cancer patients.

DEFICIENCY SYMPTOMS

Low Vitamin A is a leading cause of blindness in the world. Other symptoms include poor night vision, recurrent infections, skin problems and other subtle health complaints.

WHEN MORE IS NEEDED. Pregnancy, breastfeeding, vegetarian diets, infections, fevers, poor vision, stress and liver problems.

B COMPLEX VITAMINS

The B-complex vitamins, along with Vitamin C, are the water soluble vitamins. They play so many roles in the body it is difficult to list them all here. Among the major ones are sugar metabolism, energy production in the cells, liver function, brain activity and many others. Most of the B vitamins speed up a sluggish oxidation rate except for choline and inositol, which slow it down.

THIAMIN OR B1

Chinese medical textbooks as far back as 2700 BC describe a disease called beri beri, caused by eating a diet high in white rice. Symptoms were mostly neurological including peripheral neuritis, followed eventually by death. In 1926, scientists found a substance in rice bran that reverses Beri Beri and gave it the name of vitamin B1 or thiamine.

FOOD SOURCES
Among the best sources are rice polishings, wheat germ, liver, eggs, brewers yeast, nutritional yeast and other organ meats.

Vegetables and fruits are very poor sources. For this reason, vegetarians are often low in this vitamin and this tends to shorten their lives.

FUNCTIONS
Thiamine is involved in energy production, nerve conduction, and carbohydrate metabolism. It is also required for aerobic metabolism, which means the use of oxygen in the body to heal and produce energy.

This vitamin is used in megadose therapies, at times, for schizophrenia, depression, lumbago, sciatica, facial paralysis and other conditions with some success. This would indicate that some people have a metabolic defect and need more of it. However, it is also possible that toxic metals or intestinal defects are the reason why some people seem to benefit from high doses of B1.

DEFICIENCY SYMPTOMS
Fatigue, depression, low body temperature, anxiety, constipation, weight loss or gain, nerve pain or numbness, retarded growth, anorexia, digestive complaints, muscle weakness, low reflexes, circulatory problems, memory loss, and muscle atrophy.

WHEN MORE IS NEEDED
Pregnancy, breastfeeding, heavy exercise, alcohol consumption, high carbohydrate diet, processed food diets, vegetarian diets, old age, digestive disturbances, and use of antibiotics.

RIBOFLAVIN OR B2
This was discovered around 1930 as a growth factor found in some yeasts.

FOOD SOURCES
The best sources are organ meats such as liver, brewers yeast, nutritional yeast and some dairy products.

FUNCTIONS
Energy production in the mitochondria. It is also helpful for fetal development of a baby, the eyes and the skin.

DEFICIENCY SYMPTOMS
These include fatigue and perhaps cracks on the sides of the mouth called cheilosis. There is no major disease associated with deficiency, as there is for some of the other B vitamins.

WHEN IS MORE NEEDED
Pregnancy, breastfeeding, liver problems, alkaline conditions of the water, food or body, heavy exercise, antibiotic use, digestive disturbances, fevers, hyperthyroidism, trauma and stress. Most older people need more as well.

NIACIN, NIACINIMIDE, NICOTINIC ACID OR VITAMIN B3

These are a very critical vitamin for energy production, brain functioning and hundreds of other chemical reactions in the body.

FOOD SOURCES

Peanuts, brewers yeast, nutritional yeast, organ meats, tuna fish, halibut, swordfish, chicken and turkey. (I do not recommend eating tuna fish, halibut, or swordfish due to their high mercury content.) Fruits and vegetables are poor sources.

FUNCTIONS

Tissue metabolism, carbohydrate and energy production, fat metabolism.

DEFICIENCY SYMPTOMS

Common symptoms are fatigue, low stomach acid, retarded growth, depression, schizophrenia, other mental problems, weakness, poor appetite, indigestion, skin diseases, dark pigmentation of the skin, diarrhea, swollen tongue, irritability, headaches, sleep difficulties, memory loss.

If the deficiency gets worse, a disease occurs called pellagra. It is characterized by the four Ds: diarrhea, dermatitis, dementia and death. Many cases of depression, anxiety and other so-called emotional illness can be caused by a mild deficiency of this and other B vitamins.

WHEN IS MORE NEEDED

Pregnancy, breastfeeding, old age, high-calorie diets, malnutrition, skin diseases, perhaps high cholesterol, high intake of corn, digestive disturbances and stress.

PANTOTHENIC ACID OR B5

This is essential for energy production in the body. It is especially important to manufacture the adrenal hormones such as adrenalin, noradrenaline, aldosterone and cortisone. The glands are weak in most people today, in part due to low levels of pantothenic acid in many people.

FOOD SOURCES

Brewers yeast, liver, kidney, eggs, peanuts, wheat germ, herring and royal jelly. Vegetarians are often tired due to low levels of this vitamin.

FUNCTIONS

The main ones are cellular energy production and adrenal hormone production. However, it is also involved in stress resistance, fat metabolism, acetylcholine synthesis and antibody synthesis. It also works closely with the other B vitamins to prevent B vitamin deficiencies.

DEFICIENCY SYMPTOMS

These include fatigue, weakness, muscle tightness, neuromotor disturbances such as tremors, heart disease, digestive problems, low resistance to stress and infections, and depression.

WHEN MORE IS NEEDED

Stress, aging, arthritis, illnesses of all kinds, malabsorption syndromes, weakness, depression, antibiotic use and burning feet syndrome.

PYRIDOXINE, PYRIDOXYL-5 PHOSPHATE OR VITAMIN B6.

This a very important chemical in the body. It is required for the synthesis of proteins and amino acids. It is also involved in the metabolism of all foods—fats, proteins, sugars and starches.

FOOD SOURCES

These include liver, herring, salmon, brewers yeast, nuts, wheat germ brown rice and blackstrap molasses. (I do not recommend eating too much salmon or blackstrap molasses, due to mercury in fish and too much iron in molasses.)

FUNCTIONS

Vitamin B6 is important for protein synthesis, as well as the metabolism of fats, carbohydrates and sugars. It is also an excellent copper antagonist.

DEFICIENCY SYMPTOMS

There is no specific disease associated with deficiency. However, most people have too little vitamin B6. This can cause fatigue, copper toxicity, skin diseases, depression, convulsions, seizures, connective tissue problems, tissue breakdown in general, and any high copper symptoms. Low levels can cause a hypochromic, microcytic anemia that looks exactly like an iron deficiency or a copper imbalance anemia. B6 deficiency may cause some cases of carpal tunnel syndrome.

WHEN MORE IS NEEDED

Pregnancy, breastfeeding, irradiation or having a lot of x-rays, inborn errors of metabolism, toxic metal poisoning, especially copper, high protein diets and stress. Slow oxidation and aging increase the need as well in many cases.

CYNACOBALMIN OR METHYLCOBALAMIN OR VITAMIN B12.

This an unusual vitamin in that it is hard to absorb for many people, especially as they age.

FOOD SOURCES

Kidney, liver, brain, heart, milk, beef, egg yolk, clams, oysters, sardines, salmon, and herring. (I do not recommend eating any clams or oysters due to high levels of toxic metals. Also, all fish should be restricted to one time a month, except sardines, maximum due to mercury contamination.)

FUNCTIONS

Vitamin B12 is an extremely important substance for protein synthesis, the nervous system. blood formation, and for fat and nucleic acid synthesis.

DEFICIENCY SYMPTOMS

Low levels, which are very common in older people and those under stress, cause nervous ticks, memory loss, dementia, Alzheimer's like conditions, fatigue, weakness, possibly permanent nerve damage, hyperactivity, and other vague complaints. It also can cause a macrocytic, macrochromic anemia called pernicious anemia.

WHEN MORE IS NEEDED

Pregnancy, breast feeding, infancy and childhood, pernicious anemia, high Vitamin C intake, loss of intrinsic factor in the stomach (usually due to stress or aging), low stomach acid, malabsorption syndromes, anorexia, vegetarian diets, low meat intake, neuropathy, alcohol use, aging, stress, digestive disturbances and perhaps antibiotic use.

NOTE: All vegetarians must take a Vitamin B12 supplement, as it is such a critical vitamin and deficiency can occur slowly and insidiously. Some vegetarians claim they obtain it from seaweed or other vegetable sources, but I would not rely on this, since vegetables are very poor sources.

Vitamin B12 is the only vitamin that often must be given intramuscularly or intravenously instead of by mouth. This is because it requires something called intrinsic factor in the stomach for its absorption. This chemical is often low in older people, those with intestinal disorders (which includes many people), and especially those under stress.

FOLIC ACID

This has many critical functions in the body, mostly involved with the synthesis of nucleic acids, which are chemicals needed in the nucleus of the cells. Many medical drugs, especially cancer chemotherapy agents, can deplete folic acid and this may be how they work to some degree. However, this also makes them very toxic for the body.

FOLIC ACID SUPPLEMENTS

Sadly, folic acid levels in vitamin pills are restricted by law to very low levels. Although the rationale for this made sense—to prevent B12 anemia from being masked by high levels of folic acid—the result is even worse. People who take vitamins are not getting enough folic acid, though they believe they are because they are taking a supplement.

FOOD SOURCES

Liver, kidney, yeast, green vegetables, legumes or dried beans, peanuts, mushrooms, beef, veal, brewers yeast, and egg yolk.

FUNCTIONS

Nucleic acid synthesis and metabolism, growth, methylation, and porphyrin synthesis. These are pigments that are very important for health. It is also involved in regulating cell division in the nucleus of the cells. Thus it may be important for cancer prevention. It is also a powerful copper antagonist, and it may increase the oxidation or metabolic rate.

DEFICIENCY SYMPTOMS

Birth defects, macrocytic anemia, red and swollen tongue, diarrhea, gastrointestinal ulcers or other lesions, malabsorption, celiac disease or gluten intolerance, and pancytopenia (a blood disorder).

WHEN MORE IS NEEDED

Pregnancy, illness, some anemias, old age, alcohol use, mental illness, retardation, gastric disturbance, malabsorption, diarrhea, antibiotic and some anti-convulsant therapy, leukemia, cheilosis (cracks at the sides of the mouth), infections and Hodgkin's disease.

PABA—OR PARAMINOBENZOIC

PABA is one of the less essential B vitamins. It is also known as Vitamin H or Vitamin B7. It is helpful for the skin, hair and nails, and may reverse or prevent premature graying of the hair. A supplement may help with fatigue, depression, irritability, and other common B-vitamin deficiency states.

BIOTIN

Biotin is considered one of the less important B-complex vitamins, but this is a mistake. It is commonly deficient in the population, especially in slow oxidizers. One reason for this is that intestinal bacteria can synthesize some biotin, but only if the intestinal flora is correct, which is often not the case. As a result, many people suffer from a sub-clinical deficiency of this critical B-complex vitamin.

FOOD SOURCES

Excellent sources are egg yolk, liver, kidney, brewers yeast, whole grains and peanuts. It should be produced in the intestines, but often this does not occur adequately today due to a damaged intestinal tract and incorrect intestinal flora, especially if one has recently taken an antibiotic.

Eating raw egg whites can induce a biotin deficiency. Cooking the egg white, even for 2 or 3 minutes, destroys avidin, a chemical that interferes with biotin.

FUNCTIONS

Biotin is essential for amino acid metabolism, fatty acid metabolism, protein synthesis from DNA, energy production in the Krebs energy cycle within the cells, hair, skin and nail health, the nervous system, the sex glands, and prevention of some birth defects.

DEFICIENCY SYMPTOMS

These are common today, though they usually go undiagnosed. They include dandruff, other skin disorders, fatigue, lethargy, muscle pain, hypersensitivity of the skin, and possibly hair loss.

WHEN MORE IS NEEDED

Eating raw egg whites, certain skin diseases, infants with dandruff, antibiotic or sulfa drug use, and pregnancy.

CHOLINE

Choline is an essential nutrient that is often grouped as a B-complex vitamin, although it differs from the others in some ways.

FUNCTIONS

Structural integrity of the nervous system, cell membranes and the production of a critical and calming neurotransmitter, acetylcholine. It is also the major source for methyl groups, a system of the body that has to do with the adrenal glands and keeping them functioning properly.

FOOD SOURCES

Excellent sources are cow's liver, eggs, chicken, cod fish, milk, especially raw milk, and some of the cruciferous vegetables. Vegetable oils such as soybean oil are other sources. Lecithin, made from soy oil, is a rich source of choline and inositol.

DEFICIENCY SYMPTOMS

A mild deficiency of this vitamin is very common. Symptoms can include irritability, anxiety, bipolar disorder, perhaps seizures, and an elevated ALT enzyme level. More severe deficiency causes liver disease, atherosclerosis, neural tube defects and memory problems in newborns, elevated homocysteine, higher risk for pre-eclampsia, premature birth, and low birth weight babies, a greater risk for colds, breast cancer and inflammation, and a risk of copper imbalance.

WHEN MORE IS NEEDED

Old age, endurance athletes, pregnancy, vegetarian diets, alcohol use, and diets of refined foods.

INOSITOL

This is another important B-complex substance that is usually classified as a vitamin.

FOOD SOURCES

Excellent sources are whole grains, but not white flour or white rice, nuts, beans, and fruit, especially cantaloupe, other melons and oranges.

FUNCTIONS

The main functions are regulatory or signaling activities. Inositol and related compounds help regulate insulin, calcium concentration in the bones and the blood, the cell membrane electrical potential, serotonin and cholesterol and other fat levels in the blood.

DEFICIENCY SYMPTOMS

Some studies indicate that a deficiency is associated with some cases of depression, obsessive-compulsive disorder, panic disorder, agorophobia, bulimia and bipolar disorder, although the research is thin. More may be helpful for some cases of polycystic ovary syndrome or PCOS.

WHEN MORE IS NEEDED

Generally, more is required whenever one is under stress. Particular times include pregnancy, breastfeeding, illnesses and other types of stressful situations.

NEWER B COMPLEX
PANGAMIC ACID OR VITAMIN B15

This was isolated from apricot pits in 1951 by Ernst Krebs, Jr. and his father, Ernst Krebs, Sr. It is mainly involved in energy production and it is still controversial as to whether it is an essential nutrient. Most research about it has come from the former Soviet Union, where it has been used to increase athletic performance and to help correct a number of health conditions.

NITRILOSIDES OR VITAMIN B17

This interesting substance also isolated from apricot pits by Ernst Krebs, Jr. It appears to have a specifically an anti-cancer effect. A cyanide-containing molecules releases the deadly cyanide ion only at the site of cancer in the body.

FOOD SOURCES

Include the pits of apples and many other common fruits. It has a slightly bitter taste.

DEFICIENCY SYMPTOMS

May be associated with an increased risk of cancer. Those most at risk today include the entire population. Therefore, if one eats apples, for example, chew up the pits. The pits of peaches, apricots and other fruits may also contain some B17, but you must first crack open the hard shell of the pit to obtain it.

VITAMIN C

Vitamin C is an important vitamin. It is a modified sugar and is usually made from corn, or other sugary foods. It is water soluble and does not stay long in the body, so it must be eaten daily. Most animals can synthesize enough of it, but humans often cannot, so they need to ingest some from food.

Vitamin C is found in highest concentration in the retina of the eyes and adrenal glands, as well as all the other glands of the body. However, it is present in all human tissues. It is extremely yin in oriental medical terms, but an extremely important substance in human physiology. Most people do not ingest enough of it.

FOOD SOURCES.

Vitamin C is found in most foods, but mainly in green vegetables and some fruits. Cooking food for more than about 15 minutes can destroy most of it, so raw foods are richer sources. One of the best sources is carrot juice that we recommend for everyone, about 10-12 ounces daily for adults.

FUNCTIONS

It is a powerful anti-oxidant, and required for many oxidation-reduction reactions in the cells. It is important for wound healing, formation of bone and cartilage, growth, adrenal activity, health of the capillaries and other connective tissue, and detoxification of metals and chemicals from the body.

It may have other roles, such as helping to prevent or heal many infections, particularly viral infections. It also chelates and removes toxic substances, and enhances cell respiration.

DEFICIENCY SYMPTOMS

Severe deficiency causes scurvy, a disease that was common among sailors who had little access to fresh food. The British navy figured out how to prevent or cure the problem by requiring the sailors to eat limes. This gave rise to a nickname for British sailors of limies.

Symptoms of scurvy include adrenal exhaustion, bleeding gums, bleeding or hemorrhages into the tissues from weak capillaries, and eventually breakdown of connective tissue everywhere in the body leading to death.

Today, subclinical or mild scurvy occurs in some people around the world who live on refined, cooked food diets with few fruits, vegetables or fresh food. Symptoms may include fatigue, depression, bleeding or fragile gums, and weak connective tissue that can cause tendon, ligament, artery, vein and skin problems. Other possible symptoms are achy joints, rough skin, tooth decay and bone abnormalities and deformities. Vitamin C deficiency in infants may cause a rare megaloblastic anemia.

An acute overdose often causes diarrhea, which remove the excess Vitamin C. Chronic overuse of Vitamin C can increase iron absorption, which can be toxic. It also depletes copper and many other vital minerals. This can severely unbalance body chemistry and even contribute to illnesses such as gout, infertility (low copper), kidney stones and cancer from its yin effect and mineral depletion.

WHEN MORE IS NEEDED

Scurvy, pregnancy, breast feeding, heavy metal toxicity (everyone has this to a degree), stress, trauma, allergies, old age, high protein diets, and infections of many kinds.

Vitamin C is a powerful copper antagonist. Copper oxidizes Vitamin C. Vitamin C chelates and helps remove copper, as well as all the toxic metals.

EFFECT ON THE OXIDATION RATE

Due to its action on the adrenal glands, Vitamin C always enhances the oxidation rate. More Vitamin C is found in the adrenals than anywhere else in the body.

VITAMIN D

Vitamin D is a fat-soluble and extremely important vitamin. It was discovered around 1920 as a factor in yeast and other foods that would prevent a common disease of the time called rickets. Vitamin D is receiving much more attention in the past five years because testing reveals that most people, except young children, are low in Vitamin D. This occurs in spite of living in a sunny climate and eating dairy products enriched with Vitamin D. Sunscreens can reduce Vitamin D synthesis by the skin.

Is Vitamin D a hormone? Some call Vitamin D a hormone because it seems to affect every body system. However, hormones are usually produced by a particular gland. The kidney does produce the active form of Vitamin D, but only if the precursor is supplied from food, nutritional supplements or sunshine. Therefore, I would not call Vitamin D a hormone.

FOOD SOURCES

Among the best sources are fish liver and especially fish liver oils. Some salt water fish are also high in Vitamin D. Sources that are not quite as high, but are very good include raw egg yolks and raw dairy products. It is easy to eat a raw egg yolk by soft boiling, poaching or lightly frying an egg so the yolk remain runny.

FUNCTIONS

Vitamin D has many functions. A major one is to enhance calcium and phosphorus absorption and utilization. Others include bone health, immune response, cancer prevention, cardiovascular health, and it is anti-inflammatory in a number of ways.

DEFICIENCY SYMPTOMS. Formerly, the main deficiency diseases were rickets and osteomalacia. Rickets is a malformation or retarded growth of the long bones, and low serum calcium and phosphorus. Osteomalacia can lead to bone loss.

These diseases are not common today because pasteurized milk is fortified with Vitamin D by law. In the past 20 years or so, however, scientists have discovered that although people are obtaining the minimum daily requirement of Vitamin D from their food and sunlight, more Vitamin D is needed.

Subtle deficiency symptoms seem to be related to excess cancers, heart disease, stroke, hypertension, autoimmune diseases, diabetes, depression, chronic pain, osteoarthritis, osteoporosis, muscle weakness, muscle wasting, birth defects, periodontal disease, rheumatoid arthritis, asthma, immune deficiency, weight gain, dementias and more Vitamin D may also protect against radiation damage.

Most adults need a supplement of about 5000 IU daily. While usually enough, more may help when breast feeding, with low sun exposure, improper diet, and increasing age. Children need less, in general. The general toxicity of the body may be one factor in determining how much Vitamin D supplementation is needed.

VITAMIN E

Vitamin E is a fat-soluble and very important vitamin. It was discovered in 1922 and for a number of years was called "factor X" until it was later renamed Vitamin E. Vitamin E is actually a group of factors called tocopherols and tocotrienols.

FOOD SOURCES

Fortunately, Vitamin E is found in many foods. Among the best sources are wheat germ, soybean oil, many green and yellow vegetables, yeast, sunflower seeds, margarine, and other foods.

FUNCTIONS

Vitamin E is a powerful anti-oxidant that, along with selenium and other nutrients, protects cell membranes against oxidant damage. It also protects the delicate enzymes in the mitochondria of the cells that are needed for energy production within each cell.

Vitamin E is also essential for adrenal gland activity, and for this reason, perhaps, tends to increase the oxidation or metabolic rate in all cases. Other functions include increasing the circulation and preventing certain birth defects. Vitamin E is also protective for the heart and arteries, and can prevent stroke damage if used immediately after a stroke in large doses. The reason is probably that damage to the brain is due to oxidants, and Vitamin E helps prevent this damage.

DEFICIENCY SYMPTOMS

These include anemias, creatinuria, cystic fibrosis of the pancreas, oxidant damage of the body, fatigue, impaired circulation, general poor health, poor muscle development or muscle wasting, and asthma or other lung damage due to polluted air.

WHEN MORE IS NEEDED

Pregnancy, infancy, breathing polluted air, diets of processed foods, diets high in polyunsaturated oils, and aging.

VITAMIN F—THE ESSENTIAL FATTY ACIDS

The essential fatty acids, sometimes called Vitamin F, are linoleic, linolenic, and arachadonic acids, and perhaps others. These were discovered over 100 years ago, but attracted little attention. Today they are recognized as extremely important nutrients. Most people are deficient in one type of fatty acid called the Omega-3 fatty acids. The reasons for this are:

Livestock are no longer fed grass, and are instead often raised entirely on grain that is low in Omega-3 fatty acids. This affects our commercial meats and our dairy products today. Only wild game, and grass fed meats and dairy products have any appreciable amount of Omega-3 fatty acids. Pasteurization of dairy products destroys any Omega-3 fatty acids left in our dairy products. Overcooking meats and fats also destroys many Omega-3 fatty acids. The substitution of cheap processed vegetable oils in the diet, such as corn or soybean oil, instead of butter or lard has reduced the intake of Omega-3 fatty acids.

FOOD SOURCES

Among the best sources are certain cold-water, salt-water fish such as sardines, salmon and tuna. Other sources are krill, wild game, and raw or lightly cooked grass fed meats and dairy products.

FUNCTIONS

The essential fatty acids are needed for cell membrane function and prostaglandin synthesis, primarily.

DEFICIENCY SYMPTOMS

Common symptoms are rough and dry skin, and mental symptoms such as anxiety, depression, irritability ADD, ADHD, and many others. Delayed or impaired mental development of children is a serious symptom that may be related to Omega-3 deficiency in the mother and in breast milk. Baby formula often does not contain enough Omega-3 fatty acids for optimum brain development and must be supplemented. Impaired cell membrane permeability may cause a wide variety of sometimes subtle health conditions from malnutrition and fatigue to severe problems such as cancers.

Another important symptom is inflammation, which can manifest as hundreds of symptoms such as arthritis, gastritis, arteritis, headaches, PMS, high blood pressure and many others. Hormonal imbalances are also often related to deficiencies of Omega-3 fatty acids.

WHEN MORE IS NEEDED

Most people need a daily Omega-3 supplement. Pregnancy requires more, and children must have enough to develop normally. Anyone with inflammation, hormone imbalances, PMS and mental or emotional conditions may need more. Stress may cause an increased need as well.

VITAMIN K

Vitamin K is a fat-soluble vitamin involved in blood formation, blood clotting and bone function that is found in some common vegetables, liver and kidney. It was discovered in 1929. The main forms are called K1 and K2.

FOOD SOURCES

While Vitamin K can be produced by intestinal bacteria, many people's intestinal system is so deranged that they must obtain it from food. Rich sources include cooked cabbage, cauliflower, Brussels sprouts, spinach, bean sprouts, alfalfa and soy oil. Other good sources are pork (which I do not recommend eating as it may contain parasite eggs even if well cooked), beef liver and beef kidney.

FUNCTIONS

Vitamin K is needed for blood clotting, cell growth and prevention of osteoporosis. In lower animals it also is required for energy production and in plants for photosynthesis, which is also a form of energy production.

DEFICIENCY SYMPTOMS

The main one is bleeding or hemorrhages, which can be fatal. Deficiency increases the clotting time of the blood, or can prevent clotting altogether, leading to hemorrhages. Symptoms may include easy bruising and bleeding that may be manifested as nosebleeds, bleeding gums, blood in the urine, blood in the stool, tarry black stools, or extremely heavy menstrual bleeding. The drug Coumadin or warfarin works by causing a Vitamin K deficiency to "thin the blood". Taking a lot of Vitamin K can therefore interfere with the action of this drug.

WHEN MORE IS NEEDED

Infancy, especially right after birth, breastfeeding, improper diets, antibiotic use that destroys the intestinal flora, and perhaps aging.

VITAMIN P OR BIOFLAVONIODS

The bioflavinoids are a large group of complex chemicals that are sometimes considered as vitamins, although they may not be absolutely essential for life. However, they are very important nutrients for optimum health.

Many are pigments that give color to our fruits and vegetables. The names of common ones are quercitin, rutin, hesperidin, lutein, zeoxanthin, anthocyanadins, catachins, astaxanthin and some others. All have anti-inflammatory and other effects on the body, and are found in many foods.

FOOD SOURCES

Very rich sources are the material under the skin of citrus fruits, berries, gingko biloba, red onions, parsley, whole grains such as blue and yellow corn, tea – especially white and green tea, red wine and dark bitter chocolate.

FUNCTIONS

Bioflavinoids have anti-oxidant, anti-allergic, anti-inflammatory, anti-microbial and anti-cancer activities. Much of this activity may be due to their property of stabilizing capillaries and preventing capillary fragility. They may be very protective of the heart and the cardiovascular system, as well as protective of most body systems.

DEFICIENCY SYMPTOMS

These include allergies, inflammation, infections, poor general health and possibly cancers.

WHEN MORE IS NEEDED

Inflammation, allergies, stress, pregnancy, infancy, and perhaps other situations.

MINERALS FOR LIFE

Life on our planet is built around a number of chemical elements. Important elements include calcium, magnesium, sodium, potassium, sulfur, chlorine and phosphorus. These are sometimes called the electrolytes or the macro-minerals. These are the greatest in quantity in our bodies.

CALCIUM

Found mainly in our bones, Calcium also regulates cell membrane permeability to control nerve impulse transmission and muscle contraction. It is important for blood clotting, and it regulates hormonal secretion and cell division.

Good food sources are dairy products such as cheese and yogurt. Smaller amounts are in milk, sardines, egg yolks, almonds, sesame seeds, seaweed and dark green vegetables. Goat cheese is better than cow's milk cheese for most people because cows are often fed or injected with antibiotics, female hormones and growth hormones.

MAGNESIUM

Named after the Greek city of Magnesia, where large deposits of magnesium carbonate were found centuries ago. Magnesium is the bright and shining mineral. It is required for over 500 enzymes that regulate sugar metabolism, energy production, cell membrane permeability, and muscle and nerve conduction.

Foods high in magnesium include milk, almonds, brazil nuts, cashews, whole soybeans (but not tofu, tempeh or soy protein), parsnips, wheat bran, whole grains, green vegetables, seafood, kelp and molasses.

Most people need more magnesium than they are eating because food refining strips away magnesium. Deficiency causes muscle cramps, weakness, depression and fatigue. Magnesium works closely with potassium and is a calcium antagonist.

SODIUM

The volatility and the solvent mineral. It helps regulate blood pressure, fluid balance, transport of carbon dioxide, and affects cell membrane permeability and other cell membrane functions. Deficiency causes fatigue and fluid imbalances such as low blood pressure.

Food sources include sea salt, seafood, eggs, beet greens, Swiss chard, olives, peas, and butter. Table salt is a refined junk food. Most of the minerals have been stripped away, and aluminum is often added as a flowing agent. Use natural sea salt instead.

POTASSIUM

A solvent mineral. It is also essential for regulation of the heart beat, fluid balance and to maintain blood pressure. It is also needed for buffering the blood, and cell membrane effects including nerve transmission and muscular contraction. Deficiency can cause cramps, fatigue and heart irregularities.

Good sources are herring, sardines, halibut, goose, most nuts and seeds, watercress, garlic, lentils, spinach, artichokes, lima beans, Swiss chard, avocados, buckwheat, wheat bran, molasses, and kelp. Be sure to drink the water in which you cook vegetables to obtain the potassium from the vegetables.

CHLORINE

This is a fascinating element that is found in all living tissue. Chlorine is essential for the function of cleansing the body of debris. It is also exchanged in the stomach to produce hydrochloric acid, a very necessary acid for protein digestion.

Chlorine is a member of a group of elements called the halogens. Others in this group are fluoride, iodine and bromine. The body maintains a delicate balance **between** *all these elements. Today too much chlorine, bromine and fluoride are overwhelming the iodine and causing deficiencies in our bodies. Deficiency of this element is non-existent, unlike all the other electrolytes. The reason is that chlorine is part of salt (NaCl). Most people eat too much, rather than too little table salt, as it is found in almost all prepared and processed food items today. Thus we do not focus on this element in terms of deficiencies. In contrast, excessive exposure to chlorine is a severe problem. Too much table salt and chlorinated water are the main sources. Some bleached flour products are also sources. Environmental contamination of the food, water and air are constant sources of this element, which is highly toxic in these forms.*

Minerals are perhaps the most important group of nutrients human beings require. Unlike vitamins, for example, minerals cannot be made inside the body and must come from diet or drinking water. Minerals regulate most body functions by participating in all chemical compounds in our bodies. They also form the structure of the body.

Lawrence Wilson, M.D.

SULFUR

is another cleansing and joining mineral. It is an important element for digestion and detoxification in the liver. It is needed for the joints and in all connective tissue. This includes the hair, skin and nails. Most dietary sulfur comes from sulfur-containing amino acids found mainly in animal protein foods. Good sources are eggs, meats, and often smelly foods like garlic and onions. Other sources are kale, watercress, Brussels sprouts, horseradish, cabbage cauliflower and cranberries.

Vegetarians can easily become deficient in sulfur if they do not eat eggs. Deficiency can affect hair, nails, skin, joints, energy and the ability to detoxify poisons.

PHOSPHORUS

is the fiery energy mineral. It is required for energy production, DNA synthesis and protein synthesis. It is also needed for calcium metabolism, muscle contraction and cell membrane structure.

Excellent sources include all meats, along with eggs, fish and other animal proteins. All proteins have some phosphorus in them. However, red meats and high purine proteins tend to have the most. These include organ meats, sardines, and anchovies. The latter two are not bad fish to eat. Other fish tend to be too high in mercury to make them good foods for regular use.

Other decent food sources are most nuts and seeds, chickpeas, garlic, lentils, popcorn, soybeans, and some cheeses. Animal-based sources of phosphorus are often absorbed better than grains and beans that contain phytates. These are phosphorus compounds that are not well-absorbed and that actually interfere with the absorption of calcium, magnesium and zinc, in particular. They are found in most grains and beans. This is why proper cooking and preparation of breads, beans and other foods is extremely important. Eating these foods raw eating unleavened bread is not wise for this reason.

THE TRACE ELEMENTS

Though needed in small amounts, trace minerals are absolutely essential for life. They include iron, copper, manganese, zinc, chromium, selenium, lithium, cobalt, silicon, boron and probably a dozen others that are less well-researched. Hair and blood are used to measure these elements. However, their levels in the blood are so low in most cases that blood is not often the best place to measure them, with the exception perhaps of iron.

IRON

The oxygen carrier and an energy mineral as well. It is required in hemoglobin for transporting oxygen in the blood, for detoxification and for energy production in the cells. Iron is found in lean meats, organ meats, shellfish, molasses, beans, whole-grain cereals, and dark green vegetables. Menstruating women and children on poor diets are most commonly low in iron

COPPER

A female element because it is needed more for certain functions in women. It is also called the emotional mineral, because it tends to enhance all emotions when it is high in the body. It is extremely important for women's fertility and sexual function, and its levels often varies up and down with the level of estrogen. Copper is also required for healthy arteries, pigments in hair and skin, blood formation, energy production and for neurotransmitter substances such as dopamine.

Too much copper is common today and causes a wide variety of common symptoms, especially for women but also for boys and men. Among them are depression, fatigue, acne, migraine headaches, moodiness, ADD, ADHD, autistic tendencies in babies and children, infertility, premenstrual tension and many others.

Copper sources include organ meats, nuts, seeds, beans, grains and chocolate. People with high tissue copper are often bright, young-looking, creative and emotional. This is called the copper personality type. Excess copper is more common than deficiency today, due to the use of copper water pipes, birth control pills, vegetarian diets and stress.

MANGANESE
Called the maternal element, because in a few studies, animals deprived of this element did not nurture their young. Manganese is actually a very complex mineral needed for many body functions. It is involved in cholesterol synthesis and bone growth. It is also needed for healthy tendons and ligaments, and for fat and sugar metabolism. Manganese sources are nuts, especially walnuts, bran, corn, parsley, tea and wheat germ.

Most people are deficient in biologically available manganese, as they are in zinc, selenium, chromium and other vital trace elements today. Most people also have too much of a biologically unavailable form of manganese.

ZINC
Sometimes called the gentle strength mineral. It is a male mineral, so called because it is more essential for men than for women in some ways, although it is certainly essential for women as well. it is required for hundreds of enzymes in the human body. These include the sense of taste and smell, vision, growth, sexual development, digestive enzyme production, male potency, prostate gland health, blood sugar regulation and processing of alcohol.

Zinc is very important for the joints, the skin, wound healing, and to prevent birth defects. Zinc helps prevent diabetes, acne, epilepsy and childhood hyperactivity, and helps detoxify heavy metals. Adequate zinc has a calming effect and is needed to regenerate all body tissues.

Refined food is very low in zinc. According to Dr. Carl Pfeiffer, MD, Ph.D, the entire human population is borderline zinc deficient. There are very few excellent sources of zinc today. Among the best are red meats, organ meats and some seafood that I do not recommend because it is too high in toxic metals. Other sources that are not quite as good are poultry such as chicken and tur-

key, eggs, wheat, oatmeal, pumpkin and sunflower seeds, wheat germ and colostrum. Wheat products are not recommended as wheat has become too hybridized and is a highly inflammatory and irritating food for most people today.

Vegetarians run a high risk of zinc deficiency because they avoid red meats, in most cases. Low zinc, especially in vegetarians, tends to cause a worsening of copper toxicity. Zinc supplements are essential for everyone today, although the supplements are not as good as eating high-zinc foods, generally.

CHROMIUM
Called the blood sugar mineral. It is also an energy mineral. A desert rodent called the sand rat develops diabetes when fed a laboratory diet. When returned to the desert, the diabetes goes away. Extensive research indicates the problem with the laboratory food is a lack of chromium.

Chromium is essential to for insulin metabolism. It can also help lower cholesterol. Chromium deficiency is very common, especially in middle-aged and older people. Food sources of chromium are brewers yeast, liver, kidney, beef, whole wheat bread, wheat germ, beets, mushrooms and beer. Unfortunately, most of these foods are not recommended for various reasons. Chromium can be obtained from supplements, and this is usually the best way to make sure you get enough each day.

SELENIUM
Called the spiritual mineral because it is required for the development of certain higher brain centers. It also gives a smooth, flexible and soft quality to the personality and even to the tissues of the body. Selenium is vital for detoxification and for thyroid activity in the human body, among its many functions. It is also needed for protein synthesis, helps the body get rid of toxic cadmium and mercury, and is needed for antioxidant production (glutathione peroxidase). As an anti-oxidant, it may help prevent cancer and birth defects. Good sources of selenium are garlic, yeast, liver, eggs, wheat germ and brazil nuts. Human milk contains six times as much selenium as cow's milk.

Refined food loses a lot of selenium (and other trace elements). For example, brown rice has 15 times as much selenium as white rice. Whole wheat bread has twice as much selenium as white bread. Everyone should supplement with selenium today. The best supplement, in my view, is a food-based selenium rather than the others that are offered today.

LITHIUM

The brain protection mineral. It has a calming, balancing and protective effect on the brain and the entire nervous system. It is found in many natural foods so it is not necessary to supplement it in many cases. However, anyone who is taking an anti-depressant or any brain-altering drug, or is suffering from any brain-related problem may benefit from a natural lithium supplement such as lithium orotate. The lithium used by medical doctors for bipolar disorder is quite toxic and should be avoided if at all possible. The natural product is far less potent, but is better absorbed and much less toxic or perhaps totally non-toxic.

COBALT

The Vitamin B12 mineral. It is essential for life as part of the Vitamin B12 molecule. Vitamin B12 is required for the nervous system and blood formation. It is found in animal products. Deficiency causes anemia and a very severe dementia that can be irreversible.

Deficiency can easily occur in strict vegetarians and in those with impaired digestion or any disorder of the stomach. It is commonly deficient to some degree in elderly people whose stomach just does not absorb it very well. For this reason, I recommend that anyone over age 65 to 70 should get a periodic B12 shot, and perhaps take some sublingually as well. It is very inexpensive insurance against the serious consequences of a Vitamin B12 deficiency.

BORON

May be called the plant mineral. It is very essential for plants, though perhaps less so for human beings. Boron can help maintain female hormone production and bone integrity. Boron is found in many foods, so supplements are rarely needed, though they will help some cases of hot flashes, at times.

SILICON

Important for the bones and skin. Food sources include lettuce, parsnips, asparagus, dandelion greens, rice bran, horseradish, onion, spinach and cucumbers, and in herbs such as horsetail. Since it is in many foods, supplements are usually not needed. Silicon and selenium also are both spiritual minerals needed for higher brain activity.

IODINE

The thyroid mineral, although it is required for all the cells of the body. It is somewhat more important for women. It is needed to make thyroid hormones, and for the regulation of metabolism. It is important for women's breast health, cancer prevention and many other body functions in somewhat mysterious ways. Good sources of iodine are all fish, seafood, sea vegetables such as kelp and others. Iodine is also added to most table salt. This, however, is a junk food that is best avoided. The problem today is not so much a lack of iodine in the diet as it is an overabundance of iodine antagonists. These are chemicals in the environment that compete with and replace iodine in the body. They include all fluoride compounds, all chlorine compounds and all bromides and bromine compounds.

Unfortunately, these chemicals are everywhere today. To reduce your exposure to them, avoid all breads and baked goods (bromine), avoid tap water, even if filtered with carbon (fluorides and chlorine, perhaps) and avoid other sources of these minerals such as all fluoride toothpastes and mouthwashes, all fluoride treatments, and exposure to bleaches and other chlorine-containing products. Because it is impossible to avoid all the iodine antagonists in the environment, an *iodine supplement such as kelp is recommended for most people. If it makes you jittery, just take less. Do not use other sea vegetables or too much fish, however, as these are higher in mercury. Prescription and OTC iodine pills or liquids are not as good, in my view, because they do not contain all the other trace minerals and they are often not quite as easily absorbed as kelp. Kelp is also a natural food and the body may be more able to regulate how much it absorbs from kelp better. Taking any single-mineral products can also unbalance body chemistry if it is done for more than a few weeks to a few months.*

Trace minerals often work in pairs or triplets. The interaction of minerals in the body is a complex and interesting subject. There are many other trace minerals such as molybdenum, vanadium, bromine, germanium, nickel, tin, cesium, rubidium, strontium, gold, silver, titanium, tritium and others.

The only way to obtain all these elements is to eat natural foods grown on mineralized soil. Dr. Weston Price, DDS, studied healthy native tribes around the world. He found they were eating about 4-10 times the vitamins and minerals of the average American living on refined and processed foods.

MORE MINERALS BASICS

Minerals, unlike many vitamins and other substances, cannot be manufactured within our bodies. We must eat them daily in our diets. Furthermore, one must eat organic food to even approach the amount of minerals our bodies require for optimum health. A study in the Journal of Applied Nutrition found that organic produce purchased randomly at Chicago health food stores had an average of five times the mineral content compared to conventional produce.

Using sea salt, rather than so-called table salt, helps one to obtain trace minerals. Most of the minerals are refined out of common table salt. Good quality sea salt usually does not raise blood pressure or harm the body in any way.

Refined table salt, however, is a junk food. It often contains added toxic metals as well such as aluminum.

Other mineral-rich foods are organic vegetables, especially root vegetables. Whole organic grains, nuts and seeds, fish and good quality meats are other good sources of minerals. Fruits are not good sources, as they are mainly water, fiber and sugars.

Kelp is another excellent source of minerals that I recommend for everyone.

Mineral absorption. Many minerals are absorbed in a particular way. In the stomach, they are mixed with proteins or amino acids, which serve as carrier substances to assist their absorption. This process requires an acidic stomach and the presence of enough protein in the diet. The process is called chelating the minerals. In their chelated form, they are far more absorbable.

This is different from chelation therapy to remove toxic metals. In that process, a drug or other natural substance is ingested or injected into the body that has the capability of grabbing onto certain minerals and removing them from the body. I do not recommend this therapy in most cases.

Minerals, from calcium and magnesium to the trace elements such as zinc, are perhaps the single most important group of nutrients. They are required for every body's function, from activating muscles and nerves, to digestion, energy production and all healing and regeneration of the body.

Restoring your vital minerals is a lifetime work, but does not have to be difficult. Mainly it involves recalling that our food is generally mineral deficient, and our environment contains toxic minerals no matter where one lives.

Recommended Reading

How to Eat, Move and be Healthy!
Paul Chek
A Chek Institute Publication, 2004

Exictotoxins: The Taste that Kills
Russell L. Blaylock. M.D.
Health Press, 1994

Genetic Nutritioneering
Jeffrey S. Bland PhD
Keats Publishing, Inc., 1999

Happiness Is an Inside Job
Sylvia Boorstein
New York, Ballantine Books. 2007

Health and Nutrition Secrets That Can Save Your Life
Russell Blaylock, M.D.
Health Press, 2006

Loving-Kindness: The Revolutionary Art of Happiness
Sharon Salzberg
Shambhala, 2002

Mommy Made and Daddy too
Martha and David Kimmel
Bantam Books, 1990

Nourishing Traditions
Sally Fallon
New Trends Publishing, 2001

Nutrition and Physical Degeneration
Weston A. Price.
The Price–Pottenger Nutrition Foundation, Inc., 2006

Nutritional Balancing and Hair Mineral Analysis
Lawrence Wilson, 2010

Outsmart Your Cancer
Tanya Harter Pierce
Thoughtworks Publishing, 2004

Sauna Therapy
Lawrence Wilson, 2006

Sugar Blues
William Duffy
Warner Books, 1975

Staying Healthy with Nutrition
Elson M. Haas, MD.
Celestial Arts, 2006

The Omnivore's Dilemma
Michael Pollon
Penguin Books, 2007

The Queen of Fats
Susan Allport
University of California Press, 2006

The New Optimum Nutrition Bible
Patrick Holford
Crossing Press, 2004

What to Eat
Luise Light
McGraw Hill, 2006

Why Zebras Don't Get Ulcers
Robert Sapolsky
W.H. Freeman & Co., 1998

Your Miracle Brain
Jean Carper.
Harper Collins, 2000
The book is an outstanding read on nutrition and brain health.

Websites for Near Infrared Saunas

Near infared sauna therapy is the least expensive, safest and most powerful modality to assist in the elimination of toxic metals, toxic chemicals and chronic infections.

ARIZONA
Near Infrared Saunas
Prescott
1(888) 330-6456

Dr. Wilson
http://drlwilson.com
/SAUNAS/BUY%20FR%20SAUNA.htm

CALIFORNIA
Joel Kneale
Redding area
(510) 301-7624

ILLINOIS
Brian Richards
Urbana
(406) 322-2028,
or mailto: BJFRichards@hotmail.com

PENNSYLVANIA
Country Ray Saunas
(800) 213-0182, access code 07
or countryraysaunas@yahoo.com

TEXAS
Masako Wada
Austin
(512) 585-3268
or http://www.mypathtowellness.com
Currently offers a kit to convert a
bathtub area to a sauna.

VERMONT
Michael Goldstein
Lincoln
802-349-0501
or http://www.nearinfraredsauna.com

WASHINGTON STATE
Cedarbrook Saunas
Woodinville
(800) 426-3929 or
www.saunasauna.com

Helpful Websites for Health

www.americangrassfedbeef.com
Provides information on grass fed beef.

www.avaandersonnontoxic.com
Information on toxic free health products.

www.freshdirect.com
A company that focuses on home foods delivery in the New York Area.

www.eatwild.com
Provides information on the benefits of grass fed beef.

www.svaroopayoga.org/index.asp
Svaroopa Yoga is a gentle and relaxing form of Hatha Yoga, that is intended to bring a deep release to muscles surrounding the spine by starting with the tailbone and by progressing through each spinal area. This is a consciousness-oriented yoga that promotes healing and transformation.

http://learn.genetics.utah.edu/content/ epigenetics/nutrition
Nutrition and Epigenetics

www.vpul.upenn.edu
Provides a list of the top 10 unhealthy foods.

www.findaspring.com
Free database providing information on natural springs not only in Northa America, but in the world.

www.vivapura.com
This website sells Botija Olives.
To order call: 877-787-6457

www.realmilk.com/where2.html
Provides resources on the what and where of raw milk.

www.westonaprice.org
Independent and accurate information on health.

www.drlwilson.com
Provides hundreds of free articles on Hair tissue mineral analysis and on near infrared sauna therapy.

www.mercola.com
Provides hundreds of free articles on health and nutrition.

www.glutenfree.com
Gluten-free products and books.

www.arltma.com
This website provides information on hair tissue mineral analysis as well other valuable laboratory information.

www.seedsofdeception.com/document- Files/144.pdf.
Provides a shopping guide by brand name of genetically modified foods.

www.nongmoshoppingguide.com/SG/ TipsforAvoidingGMOs/index.cfm
Provides information on genetically modified foods.

RECOMMENDED PRODUCTS

These products are safe and may be helpful to those who participate in nutritional balancing or for anyone just interested in improving the quality of their life.

JUICERS

Champion Brand Juicer
Excellent juicer for all types of vegetables. The Vita-Mix is not recommended for juicing carrots because it mixes too much water and carrot juice and does not extract enough minerals.

Hippocrates Brand Juicer
Juices vegetables and wheat grass—Electrical unit

Wheateena
Electric unit that juices wheat grass, sprouts, greens, herbs and other kinds of vegetables. It also makes great nut butters, bean and seed paste for spreads and dressings.

Tornado Stainless Wheatgrass Juicer
Stainless steel manual wheatgrass juicer. Just clamp it to the table.

Q-Link
Helps to reduce the effects of electromagnetic stress. Available at www.amazon.com or from www.qlinkproducts.com

HEALTHFUL SHAMPOOS

Bentley Organic Shampoo
All varieties

Jason (brand)
Tee Tree Shampoo and Conditioner for babies, or anyone.

Burts Bees Products
They include: Baby Bee Talc-Free Dusting Powder, Buttermilk Bath Soak, Bubble Bath and Shampoo and Wash

HEALTHFUL CONDITIONERS

Organic Excellence Chemical free Mint Conditioner

SOAPS

Dr. Bronner's Liquid Soap
(all scents are recommended)

SUNSCREEN PRODUCTS

Soleo Organics Sunscreen Brand available on www.amamzon.com This product is an excellent choice because it has no chemical UV absorbers, no synthetic preservative, no titanium dioxide, no benzoates, no petrochemicals, not artificial fragrances. It contains only natural and organic ingredients.
A great product for both young and old.

LESS TOXIC COSMETICS

Dr. Hauschka Products
Certified natural, containing the highest quality plant and mineral ingredients.

ENDNOTES

1. Pollan, Michael, (2008), In Defense of Food. New York: Penguin Press.

2. Fallon, S. & Enig, M. (1999). Nourishing Traditions. Washington, DC: New Trends Publishing.

3. If you would like to read more in depth information about nutritional balancing science and hair tissue mineral analysis, please refer to Appendix A and B.

4. If you would like to read more in depth information about nutritional balancing science and hair tissue mineral analysis, please refer to Appendix A and B.

5. Wilson, Larry, (2009). Nutritional Balancing and Hair Tissue Mineral Analysis.

6. http:// www.faqs.org/health/Healthy -Living-V1/Enviornmental-Health- Endocrine-disrupters.html

7. http://www.ncbi.nlm.nih.gov/pubmed/8901853

8. Bowden,J. (2007). The 150 Healthiest Foods on Earth. Gloucester: Fair Winds Press.

9. Wilson, L. (2009). Nutritional balancing and hair Mineral Analysis, Wilson,L. Yin and Yang for Health. Retrieved, January 5, 2009 from http://www.drlwilson.com

10. Ibid.

11. Bowden,J. (2007). The 150 Healthiest Foods on Earth. Gloucester: Fair Winds Press.

12. Ibid.

13. Chek, P. (2004). How to Move and Be Healthy! San Diego: A C.H.E. K. Institute Publication.

14. http://www.eatwild.com/

15. Allport, S. (2006). The Queen of Fats. Berkeley: University of California Press.

16. Hass, E. (2006) Staying healthy with Nutrition. Berkeley: Celestial Press.

17. Ibid.

18. Ibid.

19. Weston price.org/Agriculture-an-Nutrition.html

"As soil fertility declines, it becomes harder for the farmer to produce a crop in what once was a productive soil. The industry came up with the answer to enable the farmer to maintain or even increase his yield as soil fertility declined. Their answer was hybrid crops. Hybrid crops are known for their vigor and increased insect and disease resistance. Since a farmer can't save seeds from a hybrid crop to grow the same crop the next year, there had to be some benefit in hybrid seeds to persuade the farmer to purchase new seeds each year. Obviously high yield along with insect and disease resistance is good for the farmer's income. Nobody seems to have asked whether this meant anything in the way of nutritional value for the consumer. In order to maintain yields as soil fertility declines, it becomes necessary to grow crops that place less demand on the soil fertility for their growth. Crops that require less nutrition from the soil will thrive while crops that require higher nutrition from the soil will fail The first way farmers accomplished this was to switch from legume crops to non-legume crops. The introduction of hybrids has provided the farmer with a new means to maintain his yield while growing the same crop. Dr. Albrecht explained how the hybridization of corn fits the pattern of increased bulk yield at the cost of reduced protein content. Hybrid corn can grow where old fashioned open pollinated corn fails because the hybrid requires less nutrition in the way of minerals from the soil to survive. This attribute has been accomplished by cross breeding to alter the genetics, reducing the protein output of the corn while increasing the carbohydrate output. While the hybrid demands less from the soil to survive, it also produces less protein and more carbohydrate. This is effectively no different from growing the crop with more potassium to increase yield per acre at the expense of total nutritional value per acre. If a crop demands less from the soil fertility, it produces less nutrition."

20. Wilson, L. retrieved, January 7, 2009, from http://www.drlwilson.com

21. Wilson, L. retrieved, December 19, 2008 from http://www.drlwilson.com

22. Duffey, William, (1975). Sugar Blues. New York: Grand Central Press.

23. Abrahamson, E & Pezet, A, (1974). Body Mind and Sugar. New York: Pyramid Press.

24. Appleton, Nancy. (1996). Lick the Sugar Habit. Avery.

25. Duffey, William, (1975). Sugar Blues. New York: Grand Central Press.

26. Soy Alert, Retrieved January 4, 2009, from http://www.westonaprice.org/soy/index.html

27. Ibid.

28. Chek, P. (2004). How to Move and Be Healthy! San Diego: A C.H.E. K. Institute Publication.

29. Smith, Jefferey.(2003). Seeds of Deception, Fairfield: Yes! Books.

30. Smith, Jeffrey. (2007). Genetic Roulette, Fairfield:Yes! Books.

31. Wilson, Larry, (2010). Nutritional balancing and Hair tissue mineral analysis.

32. Seyle, Hans, (1956) The Stress of Life, New York: McGraw Hill.

33. Wilson, Larry, (2010). Nutritional balancing and Hair tissue mineral analysis.

34. Ibid.

35. Certified Raw Milk means an authorizing agency has certified the product for the cleanliness of its operation. The certification process is very stringent. Because Certified Raw producers are almost always very small dairies, the problems encountered by large factory-farmed dairy operations do not exist. The cows are healthy, and are not pushed into over-production and therefore antibiotics need not be used. When you buy Certified Raw Milk, please note, that the cows are living in a natural environment, mostly on pasture, and are being treated humanely.

36. See Appendix A for more information.

37. Blaylock, R. (2006). Health and Nutrition Secrets That Can Save your Life. Albuquerque: Health Press.

38. Wilson, L. Having Healthy Children, retrieved on December 14, 2008, from http://www.drlwilson.com

39. Holford, P. (2004). The New Optimum Nutrition Bible. Berkeley: Crossing Press.

40. Ibid.

41. Wilson, L. Having Healthy Children, retrieved on December 14, 2008, from http://www.drlwilson.com

42. Ibid.

43. Kimmel M. & Kimmel D. (1990) Mommy Made and Daddy Too! New York: Bantam Books.

44. Wilson, L. Having Healthy Children, retrieved on December 14, 2008, from http://www.drlwilson.com

45. Outcome-based comparison of Ritalin versus food-supplement treated children with ADHD. Altern Med Rev. 2003 Aug;8(3):319-30.

46. In the 1970's, Dr. Benjamin Feingold found that many of the hyperactive children were allergic to artificial flavors, colorings, preservatives, and the salicylic compounds found in aspirin and many berry fruits. An association bearing his name continues even today to educate parents about the Feingold program, which eliminates these artificial additives from a child's lifestyle, and can help children with various kinds of ailments.

47. Wilson, L. Having Healthy Children, retrieved on December 14, 2008, from http://www.drlwilson.com

With health, everything is a source of
pleasure; without it, nothing else, whatever
it may be, is not enjoyable. Health is
by far the most important element in
human happiness.

Arthur Schopenhauer

INDEX

INDEX *(continued)*

INDEX (continued)

ABOUT THE AUTHOR

JOY FELDMAN

My path has not been a straight one. In college, I envisioned myself passionately involved in the field of law and legislation as I believed that was how I could make a significant impact on a large group of people. Studying history at the undergraduate level and then graduate training in the area of public policy and education both at the University of Pennsylvania, I believed it was my route to making a difference in society. To further my training, I then went on to earn a Law Degree at the University of Miami and worked in the area of Corporate Law, focusing on Mergers and Acquisitions, SEC filings and Contract work. With a strong interest in the area of healthcare, I conducted legal research for a top tier medical institution working on health care related issues. I enjoyed my work, but it was not personally satisfying, so I sought out a different opportunity in the field of legislation and public policy. In my new role, I worked on writing legislation for a Fortune 500 Health Care Company, overseeing a successful house bill from start to finish, lobbying at the state capital, setting goals with legislators, and authoring legal documentation regarding auxiliary healthcare professionals.

While I enjoyed the process of facilitating change in our society, I did not enjoy its political bent. Realizing that politics and law were not my callings, I pursued work in the area of education, volunteering in underprivileged cities, teaching children math, reading, and the importance of health and nutrition. As I began tutoring children in schools, I noticed that many children were unnourished and could not concentrate on their studies. I advocated for better nutrition and brought in a health expert to discuss food, health, and healing. Having learned from my own experience that nutrition was vitally important to my healing, and seeing how it was affecting children in schools, I began to consider health as my new path.

I went back to school and began post-graduate training in Nutrition. It included pursuing a Masters Degree in Holistic Nutrition as well as one-on-one mentoring by Dr. Lawrence Wilson, a physician, who studied directly under Dr. Paul Eck, a scientist and researcher who is considered one of the foremost authorities on nutrition and on the science of mineral balancing. Under Dr. Wilson's tutelage, I earned a certificate in Biochemical Nutritional Balancing Science from Westbrook University and also completed Advanced Training in Biochemical Nutritional Balancing Science. I am now an instructor/teacher of Nutritional Balancing Science where I educate new practitioners (e.g. physicians, chiropractors, and mid-level providers) on interpretation of hair charts, lend guidance on nutritional protocols, assist in teaching lifestyle changes, and explain how to recommend supplements based on interpretation of each individual's biochemistry. After beginning my private practice in nutritional balancing science, I was asked by some of my clients to put together a book, including the recipes for this program. Never did I imagine that this adventure would lead me to write two more books where I would touch not only adults, but children as well. I have thoroughly enjoyed this journey and am humbled by what I have learned.

Although I did not travel on a straight path, I did learn that life cannot be explained by perfectly linear predictability. It is mysterious, messy, and muddied and yet, these experiences have inspired me to live life with truth, courage and grace.

In 1993, I moved to Rhode Island with my husband, Michael, an Orthopedic Surgeon. I have two lovely children and one funny Springer Spaniel.

If you are interested in learning more about hair tissue mineral analysis and nutritional balancing, feel free to contact me at www.joyfeldman.com and if you would like visit my blog, see www.joyfeldman.com/blog/ Please check www.drlwilson.com for additional articles and information on nutritional balancing science and hair tissue mineral analysis.